# GCSE
# Combined Science
# Chemistry

No doubt about it, the Chemistry part of GCSE Combined Science is tough. Not to worry — this CGP book has it covered, from facts and theory to practical skills.

What's more, each topic in this book includes exam-style practice, *and* we've put in a full set of Chemistry practice papers to help you sharpen up your exam skills.

There are fully-worked answers at the back too, so it's easy to check how you're doing and find out how to pick up the best marks possible!

### How to access your free Online Edition

This book includes a free Online Edition to read on your PC, Mac or tablet.
You'll just need to go to **cgpbooks.co.uk/extras** and enter this code:

1150 3148 6296 0353

By the way, this code only works for one person. If somebody else has used this book before you, they might have already claimed the Online Edition.

# Complete
# Revision & Practice
Everything you need to pass the exams!

# Contents

Throughout this book you'll see grade stamps like these:

These grade stamps help to show how difficult the questions are.
Remember — to get a top grade you need to be able to answer **all** the questions, not just the hardest ones.

In the real exams, some questions test how well you can write (as well as your scientific knowledge).
In this book, we've marked these questions with an asterisk (*).

## Topic 4 — Chemical Changes

## Topic 5 — Energy Changes

## Topic 6 — The Rate and Extent of Chemical Change

## Topic 7 — Organic Chemistry

## Topic 8 — Chemical Analysis

## Topic 9 — Chemistry of the Atmosphere

## Topic 10 — Using Resources

## Practical Skills

## Practice Exams

Published by CGP

Editors: Mary Falkner, Robin Flello, Emily Howe, Paul Jordin, Christopher Lindle and Ciara McGlade.

Contributors: Mike Bossart and Paddy Gannon.

From original material by Richard Parsons.

With thanks to Katie Braid, Katherine Faudemer, Sophie Scott and Hayley Thompson for the proofreading.

With thanks to Ana Pungartnik for the copyright research.

Data used to construct table on page 137 contains public sector information licensed under the Open Government License v3.0. http://www.nationalarchives.gov.uk/doc/open-government-licence/version/3/

Printed by Elanders Ltd, Newcastle upon Tyne.

Clipart from Corel®

## The Scientific Method

This section <u>isn't</u> about how to 'do' science — but it does show you the way <u>most scientists</u> work.

## Scientists Come Up With **Hypotheses** — Then **Test** Them

1) Scientists try to <u>explain</u> things. They start by <u>observing</u> something they don't understand.

2) They then come up with a <u>hypothesis</u> — a possible <u>explanation</u> for what they've observed.

3) The next step is to <u>test</u> whether the hypothesis might be <u>right or not</u>. This involves making a <u>prediction</u> based on the hypothesis and testing it by <u>gathering evidence</u> (i.e. <u>data</u>) from <u>investigations</u>. If <u>evidence</u> from <u>experiments</u> backs up a prediction, you're a step closer to figuring out if the hypothesis is true.

About 100 years ago, scientists hypothesised that atoms looked like this.

## **Several Scientists** Will **Test** a Hypothesis

1) Normally, scientists <u>share</u> their <u>findings</u> in <u>peer-reviewed journals</u>, or at <u>conferences</u>.

2) <u>Peer-review</u> is where <u>other scientists</u> check results and scientific explanations to make sure they're 'scientific' (e.g. that experiments have been done in a sensible way) <u>before</u> they're published. It helps to <u>detect false claims</u>, but it doesn't mean that findings are <u>correct</u> — just that they're not wrong in any <u>obvious</u> way.

3) Once other scientists have found out about a hypothesis, they'll start basing their <u>own predictions</u> on it and carry out their <u>own experiments</u>. They'll also try to <u>reproduce</u> the original experiments to <u>check the results</u> — and if all the experiments in the world <u>back up</u> the <u>hypothesis</u>, then scientists start to think the hypothesis is <u>true</u>.

4) However, if a scientist does an experiment that <u>doesn't fit</u> with the hypothesis (and other scientists can reproduce the results) then the hypothesis may need to be <u>modified</u> or <u>scrapped</u> altogether.

After more evidence was gathered, scientists changed their hypothesis to this.

## If **All** the **Evidence** Supports a Hypothesis, It's **Accepted** — For Now

1) <u>Accepted hypotheses</u> are often referred to as <u>theories</u>. Our <u>currently accepted</u> theories are the ones that have survived this 'trial by evidence' — they've been <u>tested many times</u> over the years and <u>survived</u>.

2) However, theories <u>never</u> become totally indisputable <u>fact</u>. If <u>new evidence</u> comes along that <u>can't be explained</u> using the existing theory, then the hypothesising and testing is likely to <u>start all over again</u>.

Now we think it's more like this.

## Scientific models are constantly being refined...

The <u>scientific method</u> has been <u>developed</u> over time. Aristotle (a Greek philosopher) was the first person to realise that theories need to be based on <u>observations</u>. Muslim scholars then introduced the ideas of creating a <u>hypothesis</u>, <u>testing</u> it, and <u>repeating</u> work to check results.

# Models and Communication

Once scientists have made a <u>new discovery</u>, they <u>don't</u> just keep it to themselves.  Oh no.  Time to learn about how scientific discoveries are <u>communicated</u>, and the <u>models</u> that are used to represent theories.

## Theories Can Involve **Different Types** of **Models**

1) A <u>representational model</u> is a <u>simplified description</u> or <u>picture</u> of what's going on in real life.  Like all models, it can be used to <u>explain observations</u> and <u>make predictions</u>.  E.g. the Bohr model of an atom is a simplified way of showing the arrangement of electrons in an atom (see p.32).  It can be used to explain trends down groups in the periodic table.

*Scientists test models by carrying out experiments to check that the predictions made by the model happen as expected.*

2) <u>Computational models</u> use computers to make <u>simulations</u> of complex real-life processes, such as climate change.  They're used when there are a <u>lot</u> of different <u>variables</u> (factors that change) to consider, and because you can easily <u>change their design</u> to take into account <u>new data</u>.

3) All models have <u>limitations</u> on what they can explain or predict.  E.g. <u>ball and stick models</u> (a type of spatial model) can be used to show how ions are arranged in an ionic compound.  One of their limitations is that they <u>don't show</u> the <u>relative sizes</u> of the ions (see p.49).

## Scientific Discoveries are **Communicated** to the **General Public**

Some scientific discoveries show that people should <u>change their habits</u>, or they might provide ideas that could be <u>developed</u> into new <u>technology</u>.  So scientists need to <u>tell the world</u> about their discoveries.

Technologies are being developed that make use of <u>fullerenes</u> (see p.59).  These include <u>drug delivery systems</u> for use in medicine.  Information about these systems needs to be communicated to <u>doctors</u> so they can <u>use</u> them, and to <u>patients</u>, so they can make <u>informed decisions</u> about their <u>treatment</u>.

## Scientific **Evidence** can be **Presented** in a **Biased Way**

1) Scientific discoveries that are reported in the <u>media</u> (e.g. newspapers or television) <u>aren't</u> peer-reviewed.

2) This means that, even though news stories are often <u>based</u> on data that has been peer-reviewed, the data might be <u>presented</u> in a way that is <u>over-simplified</u> or <u>inaccurate</u>, making it open to <u>misinterpretation</u>.

3) People who want to make a point can sometimes <u>present data</u> in a <u>biased way</u> (sometimes <u>without knowing</u> they're doing it).  For example, a scientist might overemphasise a relationship in the data, or a newspaper article might describe details of data <u>supporting</u> an idea without giving any evidence <u>against</u> it.

## Companies can present biased data to help sell products...

Sometimes a company may only want you to see half of the story so they present the data in a <u>biased way</u>.  For example, a pharmaceutical company may want to encourage you to buy their drugs by telling you about all the <u>positives</u>, but not report the results of any <u>unfavourable studies</u>.

# Issues Created by Science

Science has helped us <u>make progress</u> in loads of areas, from medicine to space travel.
But science still has its <u>issues</u>. And it <u>can't answer everything</u>, as you're about to find out.

## Scientific Developments are Great, but they can Raise Issues

Scientific <u>knowledge is increased</u> by doing experiments. And this knowledge leads to <u>scientific developments</u>, e.g. new technologies or new advice. These developments can create <u>issues</u> though. For example:

<u>Economic issues:</u> Society <u>can't</u> always <u>afford</u> to do things scientists recommend (e.g. investing in alternative energy sources) without <u>cutting back elsewhere</u>.

<u>Social issues:</u> Decisions based on scientific evidence affect <u>people</u> — e.g. should fossil fuels be taxed more highly? Would the effect on people's lifestyles be <u>acceptable</u>?

<u>Personal issues:</u> Some decisions will affect <u>individuals</u>. For example, someone might support <u>alternative energy</u>, but object if a <u>wind farm</u> is built next to their house.

<u>Environmental issues:</u> <u>Human activity</u> often affects the <u>natural environment</u>. For example, building a <u>dam</u> to produce electricity will change the <u>local habitat</u> so some species might be displaced. But it will also reduce our need for <u>fossil fuels</u>, so will help to reduce <u>climate change</u>.

## Science Can't Answer Every Question — Especially Ethical Ones

1) We don't <u>understand everything</u>. We're always finding out <u>more</u>, but we'll never know <u>all</u> the answers.

2) In order to answer scientific questions, scientists need <u>data</u> to provide <u>evidence</u> for their hypotheses.

3) Some questions can't be answered <u>yet</u> because the data <u>can't</u> currently be <u>collected</u>, or because there's <u>not enough</u> data to <u>support</u> a theory.

4) <u>Eventually</u>, as we get <u>more evidence</u>, we'll answer some of the questions that <u>currently</u> can't be answered, e.g. what the impact of global warming on sea levels will be. But there will always be the "<u>Should we be doing this at all?</u>"-type questions that experiments <u>can't</u> help us to answer...

Think about <u>new drugs which can be taken to boost your 'brain power'</u>.
- Some people think they're <u>good</u> as they could improve concentration or memory. New drugs could let people think in ways beyond the powers of normal brains.
- Other people say they're <u>bad</u> — they could give some people an <u>unfair advantage</u> in exams. And people might be <u>pressured</u> into taking them so that they could work more <u>effectively</u>, and for <u>longer hours</u>.

## There are often issues with new scientific developments...

The trouble is, there's often <u>no clear right answer</u> where these issues are concerned. Different people have <u>different views</u>, depending on their priorities. These issues are full of <u>grey areas</u>.

# Risk

Scientific discoveries are often great, but they can prove risky. With dangers all around, you've got to be aware of hazards — this includes how likely they are to cause harm and how serious the effects may be.

## Nothing is Completely Risk-Free

1) A hazard is something that could potentially cause harm.

2) All hazards have a risk attached to them — this is the chance that the hazard will cause harm.

3) The risks of some things seem pretty obvious, or we've known about them for a while, like the risk of causing acid rain by polluting the atmosphere, or of having a car accident when you're travelling in a car.

4) New technology arising from scientific advances can bring new risks. For example, although carbon capture is a useful way of reducing carbon dioxide emissions that contribute to global warming, there are potential risks associated with it. E.g. a large leak in the system could be harmful to humans, as well as causing environmental issues in soil, water and plants through acidification. These risks need to be considered alongside the benefits of reducing $CO_2$ emissions.

5) You can estimate the size of a risk based on how many times something happens in a big sample (e.g. 100 000 people) over a given period (e.g. a year). For example, you could assess the risk of a driver crashing by recording how many people in a group of 100 000 drivers crashed their cars over a year.

6) To make decisions about activities that involve hazards, we need to take into account the chance of the hazard causing harm, and how serious the consequences would be if it did. If an activity involves a hazard that's very likely to cause harm, with serious consequences if it does, that activity is considered high risk.

## People Make Their Own Decisions About Risk

1) Not all risks have the same consequences, e.g. if you chop veg with a sharp knife you risk cutting your finger, but if you go scuba-diving you risk death. You're much more likely to cut your finger during half an hour of chopping than to die during half an hour of scuba-diving. But most people are happier to accept a higher probability of an accident if the consequences are short-lived and fairly minor.

2) People tend to be more willing to accept a risk if they choose to do something (e.g. go scuba diving), compared to having the risk imposed on them (e.g. having a nuclear power station built next door).

3) People's perception of risk (how risky they think something is) isn't always accurate. They tend to view familiar activities as low-risk and unfamiliar activities as high-risk — even if that's not the case. For example, cycling on roads is often high-risk, but many people are happy to do it because it's a familiar activity. Air travel is actually pretty safe, but a lot of people perceive it as high-risk.

4) People may over-estimate the risk of things with long-term or invisible effects, e.g. ionising radiation.

### The pros and cons of new technology must be weighed up...

The world's a dangerous place and it's impossible to rule out the chance of an accident altogether. But if you can recognise hazards and take steps to reduce the risks, you're more likely to stay safe.

# Designing Investigations

Dig out your lab coat and dust off your badly-scratched safety goggles... it's <u>investigation time</u>.

## Evidence Can Support or Disprove a Hypothesis

1) Scientists <u>observe</u> things and come up with <u>hypotheses</u> to test them (see p.1).
You need to be able to do the same. For example:

> <u>Observation</u>: People with big feet have spots. <u>Hypothesis</u>: Having big feet causes spots.

2) To <u>determine</u> whether or not a hypothesis is <u>right</u>, you need to do an
<u>investigation</u> to gather evidence. To do this, you need to use your hypothesis
to make a <u>prediction</u> — something you think <u>will happen</u> that you can test.
E.g. people who have bigger feet will have more spots.

*Investigations include experiments and studies.*

3) Investigations are used to see if there are <u>patterns</u> or <u>relationships</u>
between <u>two variables</u>, e.g. to see if there's a pattern or relationship
between the variables 'number of spots' and 'size of feet'.

## Evidence Needs to be Repeatable, Reproducible and Valid

1) <u>Repeatable</u> means that if the <u>same person</u> does an experiment again using
the <u>same methods</u> and equipment, they'll get <u>similar results</u>.

2) <u>Reproducible</u> means that if <u>someone else</u> does the experiment, or a <u>different</u>
method or piece of equipment is used, the results will still be <u>similar</u>.

3) If data is <u>repeatable</u> and <u>reproducible</u>, it's <u>reliable</u> and scientists are more likely to <u>have confidence</u> in it.

4) <u>Valid results</u> are both repeatable and reproducible AND they <u>answer the original question</u>.
They come from experiments that were designed to be a <u>fair test</u>...

## Make an Investigation a Fair Test By Controlling the Variables

1) In a lab experiment you usually <u>change one variable</u> and <u>measure</u> how it affects <u>another variable</u>.

2) To make it a fair test, <u>everything else</u> that could affect the results should <u>stay the same</u>
— otherwise you can't tell if the thing you're changing is causing the results or not.

3) The variable you <u>CHANGE</u> is called the <u>INDEPENDENT</u> variable.

4) The variable you <u>MEASURE</u> when you change the independent variable is the <u>DEPENDENT</u> variable.

5) The variables that you <u>KEEP THE SAME</u> are called <u>CONTROL</u> variables.

> You could find how <u>temperature</u> affects <u>reaction rate</u> by measuring the <u>volume of
> gas</u> formed over time. The <u>independent variable</u> is the <u>temperature</u>.
> The <u>dependent variable</u> is the <u>volume of gas</u> produced. <u>Control variables</u> include
> the <u>concentration</u> and <u>amounts</u> of reactants, the <u>time period</u> you measure, etc.

6) Because you can't always control all the variables, you often need to use a <u>control experiment</u>. This is
an experiment that's kept under the <u>same conditions</u> as the rest of the investigation, but <u>doesn't</u> have
anything <u>done</u> to it. This is so that you can see what happens when you don't change anything at all.

# Designing Investigations

## The **Bigger** the **Sample Size** the **Better**

1) Data based on <u>small samples</u> isn't as good as data based on large samples. A sample should <u>represent</u> the <u>whole population</u> (i.e. it should share as many of the characteristics in the population as possible) — a small sample can't do that as well. It's also harder to spot <u>anomalies</u> if your sample size is too small.

2) The <u>bigger</u> the sample size the <u>better</u>, but scientists have to be <u>realistic</u> when choosing how big. For example, if you were studying the effects of a chemical used to sterilise water on the people drinking it, it'd be great to study <u>everyone</u> who was drinking the water (a huge sample), but it'd take ages and cost a bomb. It's more realistic to study a thousand people, with a mixture of ages, gender, and race.

## Your **Equipment** has to be **Right for the Job**

1) The measuring equipment you use has to be <u>sensitive enough</u> to measure the changes you're looking for. For example, if you need to measure changes of 1 cm³ you need to use a <u>measuring cylinder</u> that can measure in <u>1 cm³</u> steps — it'd be no good trying with one that only measures 10 cm³ steps.

2) The <u>smallest change</u> a measuring instrument can <u>detect</u> is called its <u>resolution</u>. E.g. some mass balances have a resolution of 1 g, some have a resolution of 0.1 g, and some are even more sensitive.

3) Also, equipment needs to be <u>calibrated</u> by measuring a known value. If there's a <u>difference</u> between the <u>measured</u> and <u>known value</u>, you can use this to <u>correct</u> the inaccuracy of the equipment.

## Data Should be **Repeatable, Reproducible, Accurate** and **Precise**

1) To <u>check repeatability</u> you need to <u>repeat</u> the readings and check that the results are similar. You need to repeat each reading at least <u>three times</u>.

2) To make sure your results are <u>reproducible</u> you can cross check them by taking a <u>second set of readings</u> with <u>another instrument</u> (or a <u>different observer</u>).

3) Your data also needs to be <u>accurate</u>. Really accurate results are those that are <u>really close</u> to the <u>true answer</u>. The accuracy of your results usually depends on your <u>method</u> — you need to make sure you're measuring the right thing and that you don't <u>miss anything</u> that should be included in the measurements.
E.g. estimating the <u>amount of gas</u> released from a reaction by <u>counting the bubbles</u> isn't very accurate because you might <u>miss</u> some of the bubbles and they might have different <u>volumes</u>. It's <u>more accurate</u> to measure the volume of gas released using a <u>gas syringe</u> (see p.104).

| Repeat | Data set 1 | Data set 2 |
|--------|-----------|-----------|
| 1 | 12 | 11 |
| 2 | 14 | 17 |
| 3 | 13 | 14 |
| Mean | <u>13</u> | <u>14</u> |

Data set 1 is more precise than data set 2.

4) Your data also needs to be <u>precise</u>. Precise results are ones where the data is <u>all really close</u> to the <u>mean</u> (average) of your repeated results (i.e. not spread out).

# Designing Investigations

## You Need to Look out for **Errors** and **Anomalous Results**

1) The results of your experiment will always <u>vary a bit</u> because of <u>random errors</u> — unpredictable differences caused by things like <u>human errors</u> in <u>measuring</u>. E.g. the errors you make when you take a reading from a pipette are <u>random</u>. You have to <u>estimate</u> or <u>round</u> the level when it's between two marks — so sometimes your figure will be a bit above the real one, and sometimes it will be a bit below.

2) You can <u>reduce</u> the effect of random errors by taking <u>repeat readings</u> and finding the <u>mean</u>. This will make your results <u>more precise</u>.

> If there's no systematic error, then doing repeats and calculating a mean could make your results more accurate.

3) If a measurement is wrong by the <u>same amount every time</u>, it's called a <u>systematic error</u>. For example, if you measured from the very end of your ruler instead of from the 0 cm mark every time, all your measurements would be a bit small. Repeating the experiment in the exact same way and calculating a mean <u>won't</u> correct a systematic error.

4) Just to make things more complicated, if a systematic error is caused by using <u>equipment</u> that <u>isn't zeroed properly</u>, it's called a <u>zero error</u>. For example, if a mass balance always reads 1 gram before you put anything on it, all your measurements will be 1 gram too heavy.

5) You can <u>compensate</u> for some systematic errors if you know about them, e.g. if a mass balance always reads 1 gram before you put anything on it, you can subtract 1 gram from all your results.

6) Sometimes you get a result that <u>doesn't fit in</u> with the rest at all. This is called an <u>anomalous result</u>. You should investigate it and try to <u>work out what happened</u>. If you can work out what happened (e.g. you measured something wrong) you can <u>ignore</u> it when processing your results.

## Investigations Can be **Hazardous**

1) <u>Hazards</u> from science experiments might include:

> - <u>Microorganisms</u>, e.g. some bacteria can make you ill.
> - <u>Chemicals</u>, e.g. sulfuric acid can burn your skin and alcohols catch fire easily.
> - <u>Fire</u>, e.g. an unattended Bunsen burner is a fire hazard.
> - <u>Electricity</u>, e.g. faulty electrical equipment could give you a shock.

> You can find out about potential hazards by looking in textbooks, doing some internet research, or asking your teacher.

2) Part of planning an investigation is making sure that it's <u>safe</u>.

3) You should always make sure that you <u>identify</u> all the hazards that you might encounter. Then you should think of ways of <u>reducing the risks</u> from the hazards you've identified. For example:

> - If you're working with <u>sulfuric acid</u>, always wear gloves and safety goggles. This will reduce the risk of the acid coming into contact with your skin and eyes.
> - If you're using a <u>Bunsen burner</u>, stand it on a heat proof mat. This will reduce the risk of starting a fire.

## Designing an investigation is an involved process...

Collecting <u>data</u> is what investigations are all about. Designing a good investigation is really important to make sure that any data collected is <u>accurate</u>, <u>precise</u>, <u>repeatable</u> and <u>reproducible</u>.

# Processing Data

Processing your data means doing some <u>calculations</u> with it to make it <u>more useful</u>.

## Data Needs to be Organised

1) <u>Tables</u> are dead useful for <u>organising data</u>.

2) When you draw a table <u>use a ruler</u> and make sure <u>each column</u> has a <u>heading</u> (including the <u>units</u>).

## There are Different Ways of Processing Your Data

1) When you've done repeats of an experiment you should always calculate the <u>mean</u> (average). To do this <u>add together</u> all the data values and <u>divide</u> by the total number of values in the sample.

2) You might also need to calculate the <u>range</u> (how spread out the data is). To do this find the <u>largest</u> number and <u>subtract</u> the <u>smallest</u> number from it.

*Ignore anomalous results when calculating the mean and the range.*

 **The results of an experiment to find the mass of gas lost from two reactions are shown below. Calculate the mean and the range for the mass of gas lost in each reaction.**

| Test tube | Repeat 1 (g) | Repeat 2 (g) | Repeat 3 (g) | Mean (g) | Range (g) |
|---|---|---|---|---|---|
| A | 28 | 37 | 32 | (28 + 37 + 32) ÷ 3 = 32 | 37 − 28 = 9 |
| B | 47 | 51 | 60 | (47 + 51 + 60) ÷ 3 = 53 | 60 − 47 = 13 |

## Round to the Lowest Number of Significant Figures

The <u>first significant figure</u> of a number is the first digit that's <u>not zero</u>. The second and third significant figures come <u>straight after</u> (even if they're zeros). You should be aware of significant figures in calculations.

1) In <u>any</u> calculation where you need to round, you should round the answer to the <u>lowest number of significant figures</u> (s.f.) given.

2) Remember to write down <u>how many</u> significant figures you've rounded to after your answer.

3) If your calculation has multiple steps, <u>only</u> round the <u>final</u> answer, or it won't be as accurate.

 **What is the concentration, in g/dm³, of a solution of sodium chloride where 3.7 g of sodium chloride is dissolved in 0.345 dm³ of water?**

Concentration = 3.7 g ÷ 0.345 dm³ = 10.72463... = 11 g/dm³ (2 s.f.)

2 s.f.     3 s.f.     *Final answer should be rounded to 2 s.f.*

 ## Don't forget your calculator...

In the exam you could be given some <u>data</u> and be expected to <u>process it</u> in some way. Make sure you keep an eye on <u>significant figures</u> in your answers and <u>always write down your working</u>.

# Presenting Data

Once you've processed your data, e.g. by calculating the mean, you can present your results in a nice <u>chart</u> or <u>graph</u>. This will help you to <u>spot any patterns</u> in your data.

## If Your Data Comes in **Categories**, Present It in a **Bar Chart**

1) If the independent variable is <u>categoric</u> (comes in distinct categories, e.g. alkane chain length, metals) you should use a <u>bar chart</u> to display the data.

2) You also use them if the independent variable is <u>discrete</u> (the data can be counted in chunks, where there's no in-between value, e.g. number of protons is discrete because you can't have half a proton).

3) There are some <u>golden rules</u> you need to follow for <u>drawing</u> bar charts:

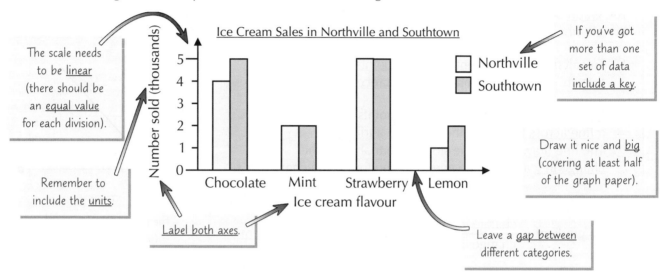

The scale needs to be <u>linear</u> (there should be an <u>equal value</u> for each division).

Remember to include the <u>units</u>.

<u>Label both axes</u>.

If you've got more than one set of data <u>include a key</u>.

Draw it nice and <u>big</u> (covering at least half of the graph paper).

Leave a <u>gap between</u> different categories.

## If Your Data is **Continuous**, Plot a **Graph**

1) If both variables are <u>continuous</u> (numerical data that can have any value within a range, e.g. length, volume, temperature) you should use a <u>graph</u> to display the data.

2) Here are the <u>rules</u> for plotting points on a graph:

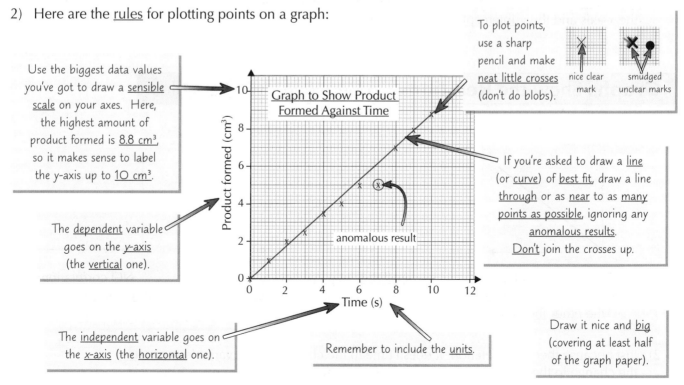

Use the biggest data values you've got to draw a <u>sensible</u> <u>scale</u> on your axes. Here, the highest amount of product formed is <u>8.8 cm³</u>, so it makes sense to label the y-axis up to <u>10 cm³</u>.

The <u>dependent</u> variable goes on the <u>y-axis</u> (the <u>vertical</u> one).

To plot points, use a sharp pencil and make <u>neat little crosses</u> (don't do blobs).

nice clear mark    smudged unclear marks

If you're asked to draw a <u>line</u> (or <u>curve</u>) of <u>best fit</u>, draw a line <u>through</u> or as <u>near</u> to as <u>many</u> <u>points as possible</u>, ignoring any <u>anomalous results</u>. <u>Don't</u> join the crosses up.

anomalous result

The <u>independent</u> variable goes on the <u>x-axis</u> (the <u>horizontal</u> one).

Remember to include the <u>units</u>.

Draw it nice and <u>big</u> (covering at least half of the graph paper).

# More on Graphs

Graph's aren't just fun to plot, they're also really useful for showing <u>trends</u> in your data.

## Graphs Can Give You a Lot of Information About Your Data

1) The <u>gradient</u> (slope) of a graph tells you how quickly the <u>dependent variable</u> changes if you change the <u>independent variable</u>.

You can use this method to calculate any rates from a graph, not just the rate of a reaction. Just remember that a rate is how much something changes over time, so *x* needs to be the time.

$$\text{gradient} = \frac{\text{change in } y}{\text{change in } x}$$

The <u>graph</u> below shows the <u>volume of gas</u> produced in a reaction against <u>time</u>. The graph is <u>linear</u> (it's a straight line graph), so you can simply calculate the <u>gradient</u> of the line to find out the <u>rate of reaction</u>.

1) To calculate the gradient, pick <u>two points</u> on the line that are easy to read and a <u>good distance</u> apart.

2) <u>Draw a line down</u> from one of the points and a <u>line across</u> from the other to make a <u>triangle</u>. The line drawn down the side of the triangle is the <u>change in y</u> and the line across the bottom is the <u>change in x</u>.

Change in y = 6.8 – 2.0 = 4.8 cm³   Change in x = 5.2 – 1.6 = 3.6 s

Rate = gradient = $\frac{\text{change in } y}{\text{change in } x}$ = $\frac{4.8 \text{ cm}^3}{3.6 \text{ s}}$ = <u>1.3 cm³/s or 1.3 cm³s⁻¹</u>

The units of the gradient are (units of *y*)/(units of *x*). cm³/s can also be written as cm³s⁻¹.

2) If you've got a <u>curved graph</u>, you can find the rate at any point by drawing a <u>tangent</u> — a straight line that touches a <u>single point</u> on a curve. You can then find the gradient of the tangent in the usual way, to give you the rate at that <u>point</u> (see page 107 for more on calculating gradients).

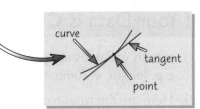

3) The <u>intercept</u> of a graph is where the line of best fit crosses one of the <u>axes</u>. The <u>x-intercept</u> is where the line of best fit crosses the *x*-axis and the <u>y-intercept</u> is where it crosses the <u>y-axis</u>.

## Graphs Show the Relationship Between Two Variables

1) You can get <u>three</u> types of <u>correlation</u> (relationship) between variables:

<u>POSITIVE correlation:</u> as one variable <u>increases</u> the other <u>increases</u>.

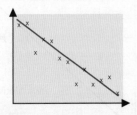

<u>INVERSE (negative) correlation:</u> as one variable <u>increases</u> the other <u>decreases</u>.

<u>NO correlation:</u> <u>no relationship</u> between the two variables.

2) Just because there's correlation, it doesn't mean the change in one variable is <u>causing</u> the change in the other — there might be <u>other factors</u> involved (see page 13).

# Units

Graphs and maths skills are all very well, but the numbers don't mean much if you don't get the <u>units</u> right.

## S.I. Units Are Used All Round the World

1) It wouldn't be all that useful if I defined volume in terms of <u>bath tubs</u>, you defined it in terms of <u>egg-cups</u> and my pal Fred defined it in terms of <u>balloons</u> — we'd never be able to compare our data.

2) To stop this happening, scientists have come up with a set of <u>standard units</u>, called S.I. units, that all scientists use to measure their data. Here are some S.I. units you'll see in chemistry:

| Quantity | S.I. Base Unit |
|---|---|
| mass | kilogram, kg |
| length | metre, m |
| time | second, s |
| amount of substance | mole, mol |

## Always Check The Values Used in Equations Have the Right Units

1) Equations (sometimes called formulas) show <u>relationships</u> between <u>variables</u>.

2) To <u>rearrange</u> an equation, make sure that whatever you do to <u>one side</u> of the equation you also do to the <u>other side</u>.

> For example, you can find the <u>number of moles</u> of something using the equation: moles = mass ÷ molar mass.
>
> You can <u>rearrange</u> this equation to find the <u>mass</u> by <u>multiplying</u> <u>each side</u> by molar mass to give: mass = moles × molar mass.

3) To use an equation, you need to know the values of <u>all but one</u> of the variables. <u>Substitute</u> the values you do know into the formula, and do the calculation to work out the final variable.

4) Always make sure the values you put into an equation have the <u>right units</u>. For example, you might want to work out the concentration of a solution. The volume of the solution will probably have been measured in $cm^3$, but the equation to find concentration uses volume in $dm^3$. So you'll have to <u>convert</u> your volume from $cm^3$ to $dm^3$ before you put it into the equation.

5) To make sure your units are <u>correct</u>, it can help to write down the <u>units</u> on each line of your <u>calculation</u>.

## S.I. units help scientists to compare data...

You can only really <u>compare</u> things if they're in the <u>same units</u>. E.g. if the concentration of an acid was measured in $g/dm^3$ and another acid in $g/cm^3$, it'd be hard to compare them.

# Converting Units

You can <u>convert units</u> using <u>scaling prefixes</u>. This can save you from having to write a lot of 0's...

## Scaling Prefixes Can Be Used for Large and Small Quantities

1) Quantities come in a huge <u>range</u> of sizes. For example, the volume of a swimming pool might be around 2 000 000 000 $cm^3$, while the volume of a cup is around 250 $cm^3$.

2) To make the size of numbers more <u>manageable</u>, larger or smaller units are used. These are the <u>S.I. base units</u> (e.g. metres) with a <u>prefix</u> in front:

| Prefix | tera (T) | giga (G) | mega (M) | kilo (k) | deci (d) | centi (c) | milli (m) | micro (μ) | nano (n) |
|---|---|---|---|---|---|---|---|---|---|
| Multiple of Unit | $10^{12}$ | $10^9$ | 1 000 000 ($10^6$) | 1000 | 0.1 | 0.01 | 0.001 | 0.000001 ($10^{-6}$) | $10^{-9}$ |

3) These <u>prefixes</u> tell you <u>how much bigger</u> or <u>smaller</u> a unit is than the base unit. So one <u>kilo</u>metre is <u>one thousand</u> metres.

4) To <u>swap</u> from one unit to another, all you need to know is what number you have to divide or multiply by to get from the original unit to the new unit — this is called the <u>conversion factor</u>.

*The conversion factor is the number of times the smaller unit goes into the larger unit.*

- To go from a <u>bigger unit</u> (like m) to a <u>smaller unit</u> (like cm), you <u>multiply</u> by the conversion factor.
- To go from a <u>smaller unit</u> (like g) to a <u>bigger unit</u> (like kg), you <u>divide</u> by the conversion factor.

5) Here are some conversions that'll be useful for GCSE Combined Science:

Energy can have units of J and kJ.

Mass can have units of kg and g.

Volume can have units of $m^3$, $dm^3$ and $cm^3$.

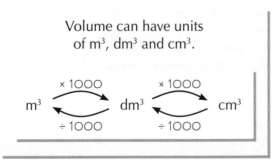

Concentration can have units of $g/dm^3$ and $g/cm^3$.

## To convert from bigger units to smaller units...

...<u>multiply</u> by the <u>conversion factor</u>, and to convert from <u>smaller units</u> to <u>bigger units</u>, <u>divide</u> by the <u>conversion factor</u>. Don't go getting this the wrong way round or you'll get some odd answers.

MATHS TIP

# Drawing Conclusions

Once you've carried out an experiment and processed your data, it's time to work out <u>what your data shows</u>.

## You Can **Only Conclude** What the Data Shows and **No More**

1) Drawing conclusions might seem pretty straightforward — you just <u>look at your data</u> and <u>say what pattern or relationship you see</u> between the dependent and independent variables.

| | Catalyst | Rate of Reaction / cm³/s | |
|---|---|---|---|
| The table on the right shows the rate of a reaction in the presence of two <u>different</u> catalysts: | A | 13.5 | CONCLUSION: Catalyst <u>B</u> makes <u>this reaction</u> go faster than catalyst A. |
| | B | 19.5 | |
| | No catalyst | 5.5 | |

2) But you've got to be really careful that your conclusion <u>matches the data</u> you've got and <u>doesn't go any further</u>.

> You <u>can't</u> conclude that catalyst B increases the rate of <u>any other reaction</u> more than catalyst A — the results might be completely different.

3) You also need to be able to <u>use your results</u> to <u>justify your conclusion</u> (i.e. back up your conclusion with some specific data).

> The rate of this reaction was <u>6 cm³/s faster</u> using catalyst B compared with catalyst A.

4) When writing a conclusion you need to <u>refer back</u> to the original hypothesis and say whether the data <u>supports it</u> or not:

> The hypothesis for this experiment might have been that catalyst B would make the reaction go <u>quicker</u> than catalyst A. If so, the data <u>supports</u> the hypothesis.

## Correlation DOES NOT Mean Cause

If two things are correlated (i.e. there's a relationship between them) it <u>doesn't</u> necessarily mean a change in one variable is <u>causing</u> the change in the other — this is <u>REALLY IMPORTANT</u> — <u>DON'T FORGET IT</u>. There are <u>three possible reasons</u> for a correlation:

1) <u>CHANCE</u>: It might seem strange, but two things can show a correlation purely due to <u>chance</u>.

> For example, one study might find a correlation between people's hair colour and how good they are at frisbee. But other scientists <u>don't</u> get a correlation when they investigate it — the results of the first study are just a <u>fluke</u>.

2) <u>LINKED BY A 3RD VARIABLE</u>: A lot of the time it may <u>look</u> as if a change in one variable is causing a change in the other, but it <u>isn't</u> — a <u>third variable links</u> the two things.

> For example, there's a correlation between <u>water temperature</u> and <u>shark attacks</u>. This isn't because warmer water makes sharks crazy. Instead, they're linked by a third variable — the <u>number of people swimming</u> (more people swim when the water's hotter, and with more people in the water you get more shark attacks).

3) <u>CAUSE</u>: Sometimes a change in one variable does <u>cause</u> a change in the other. You can only conclude that a correlation is due to cause when you've <u>controlled all the variables</u> that could affect the result.

> For example, there's a correlation between <u>smoking</u> and <u>lung cancer</u>. This is because chemicals in tobacco smoke cause lung cancer. This conclusion was only made once <u>other variables</u> (such as age and exposure to other things that cause cancer) had been <u>controlled</u>.

# Uncertainty

Uncertainty is how sure you can really be about your data. There's a little bit of maths to do, and also a formula to learn. But don't worry too much — it's no more than a simple bit of subtraction and division.

## Uncertainty is the Amount of Error Your Measurements Might Have

1) When you repeat a measurement, you often get a slightly different figure each time you do it due to random error (see page 7). This means that each result has some uncertainty to it.

2) The measurements you make will also have some uncertainty in them due to limits in the resolution of the equipment you use (see page 6).

3) This all means that the mean of a set of results will also have some uncertainty to it. You can calculate the uncertainty of a mean result using the equation:

$$\text{uncertainty} = \frac{\text{range}}{2}$$

The range is the largest value minus the smallest value (see p.8).

4) The larger the range, the less precise your results are and the more uncertainty there will be in your results. Uncertainties are shown using the '±' symbol.

 **EXAMPLE:**

**The table below shows the results of an experiment to determine the boiling point of ethanol.**
**Calculate the uncertainty of the mean.**

1) First work out the range:
   Range = 80 − 76 = 4 °C

| Repeat | 1 | 2 | 3 | mean |
|---|---|---|---|---|
| Boiling point of ethanol (°C) | 76 | 78 | 80 | 78 |

2) Use the range to find the uncertainty:
   Uncertainty = range ÷ 2 = 4 ÷ 2 = 2 °C
   So the uncertainty of the mean = 78 ± 2 °C

5) Measuring a greater amount of something helps to reduce uncertainty.

> For example, in a rate of reaction experiment, measuring the amount of product formed over a longer period compared to a shorter period will reduce the uncertainty in your results.

 **The smaller the uncertainty, the more precise your results...**

Remember that equation for uncertainty. You never know when you might need it — you could be expected to use it in the exams. You need to make sure all the data is in the same units though. For example, if you had some measurements in metres, and some in centimetres, you'd need to convert them all into either metres or centimetres before you set about calculating uncertainty.

# Evaluations

Hurrah! The end of another investigation. Well, now you have to work out all the things you did <u>wrong</u>. That's what <u>evaluations</u> are all about I'm afraid. Best get cracking with this page...

## Evaluations — Describe **How** Investigations Could be **Improved**

An evaluation is a <u>critical analysis</u> of the whole investigation.

1) You should comment on the <u>method</u> — was it <u>valid</u>? Did you control all the other variables to make it a <u>fair test</u>?

2) Comment on the <u>quality</u> of the <u>results</u> — was there <u>enough evidence</u> to reach a valid <u>conclusion</u>? Were the results <u>repeatable</u>, <u>reproducible</u>, <u>accurate</u> and <u>precise</u>?

3) Were there any <u>anomalous</u> results? If there were <u>none</u> then <u>say so</u>. If there were any, try to <u>explain</u> them — were they caused by <u>errors</u> in measurement? Were there any other <u>variables</u> that could have <u>affected</u> the results? You should comment on the level of <u>uncertainty</u> in your results too.

4) All this analysis will allow you to say how <u>confident</u> you are that your conclusion is <u>right</u>.

5) Then you can suggest any <u>changes</u> to the <u>method</u> that would <u>improve</u> the quality of the results, so that you could have <u>more confidence</u> in your conclusion. For example, you might suggest <u>changing</u> the way you controlled a variable, or <u>increasing</u> the number of <u>measurements</u> you took. Taking more measurements at <u>narrower intervals</u> could give you a <u>more accurate result</u>. For example:

<u>Enzymes</u> have an <u>optimum temperature</u> (a temperature at which they <u>work best</u>). Say you do an experiment to find an enzyme's optimum temperature and take measurements at 10 °C, 20 °C, 30 °C, 40 °C and 50 °C. The results of this experiment tell you the optimum is <u>40 °C</u>. You could then <u>repeat</u> the experiment, <u>taking more measurements around 40 °C</u> to a get a <u>more accurate</u> value for the optimum.

6) You could also make more <u>predictions</u> based on your conclusion, then <u>further experiments</u> could be carried out to test them.

*When suggesting improvements to the investigation, always make sure that you say why you think this would make the results better.*

## Always look for ways to improve your investigations

So there you have it — <u>Working Scientifically</u>. Make sure you know this stuff like the back of your hand. It's not just in the lab or the field, when you're carrying out your groundbreaking <u>investigations</u>, that you'll need to know how to work scientifically. You can be asked about it in the <u>exams</u> as well. So swot up...

# Atoms

All substances are made of <u>atoms</u>. They're really <u>tiny</u> — too small to see, even with your microscope. Atoms are so tiny that a <u>50p piece</u> contains about 77 400 000 000 000 000 000 000 of them.

## Atoms Contain **Protons, Neutrons** and **Electrons**

Atoms have a radius of about <u>0.1 nanometers</u> (that's $1 \times 10^{-10}$ m). There are a few different (and equally useful) modern models of the atom — but chemists tend to like the model below best.

A nanometer (nm) is one billionth of a meter. Shown in standard form, that's $1 \times 10^{-9}$ m. Standard form is used for showing really large or really small numbers.

### The **Nucleus**

1)  It's in the <u>middle</u> of the atom.
2)  It contains <u>protons</u> and <u>neutrons</u>.
3)  The nucleus has a <u>radius</u> of around $1 \times 10^{-14}$ m (that's around 1/10 000 of the radius of an atom).
4)  It has a <u>positive charge</u> because of the protons.
5)  Almost the <u>whole</u> mass of the atom is <u>concentrated</u> in the nucleus.

### The **Electrons**

1)  Move <u>around</u> the nucleus in electron <u>shells</u>.
2)  They're <u>negatively charged</u> and <u>tiny</u>, but they cover <u>a lot of space</u>.
3)  The <u>volume</u> of their orbits determines the size of the atom.
4)  Electrons have virtually <u>no</u> mass.

| Particle | Relative Mass | Relative Charge |
|----------|---------------|-----------------|
| Proton   | 1             | +1              |
| Neutron  | 1             | 0               |
| Electron | Very small    | −1              |

Protons are heavy and positively charged.
Neutrons are heavy and neutral.
Electrons are tiny and negatively charged.

## Number of Protons **Equals** Number of Electrons

1)  Atoms are <u>neutral</u> — they have <u>no charge</u> overall (unlike ions).
2)  This is because they have the <u>same number</u> of <u>protons</u> as <u>electrons</u>.
3)  The <u>charge</u> on the electrons is the <u>same</u> size as the charge on the <u>protons</u>, but <u>opposite</u> — so the charges <u>cancel out</u>.
4)  In an ion, the number of protons <u>doesn't equal</u> the number of <u>electrons</u>. This means it has an <u>overall charge</u>. For example, an ion with a <u>2− charge</u>, has <u>two more</u> electrons than protons.

An ion is an atom or group of atoms that has lost or gained electrons.

## **Atomic Number** and **Mass Number** Describe an Atom

1)  The <u>nuclear symbol</u> of an atom tells you its <u>atomic (proton) number</u> and <u>mass number</u>.
2)  The <u>atomic number</u> tells you how many <u>protons</u> there are.
3)  The <u>mass number</u> tells you the <u>total number</u> of <u>protons and neutrons</u> in the atom.
4)  To get the number of <u>neutrons</u>, just subtract the <u>atomic number</u> from the <u>mass number</u>.

Nuclear symbol for sodium

Mass number →23
Atomic number →11
Na
Element symbol (see next page for more on symbols).

---

## Atoms make up pretty much everything

So here we are — the nuts and bolts of what makes up an atom. This stuff is <u>super important</u> — if you get to grips with the basic facts then you'll have a better chance <u>understanding</u> the rest of chemistry.

# Elements

An <u>element</u> is a substance made up of atoms that all have the <u>same</u> number of <u>protons</u> in their nucleus.

## Elements Consist of Atoms With the Same Atomic Number

Atoms can have different numbers of protons, neutrons and electrons.
It's the number of <u>protons</u> in the nucleus that decides what <u>type</u> of atom it is.

For example, an atom with <u>one proton</u> in its nucleus is <u>hydrogen</u> and an atom with <u>two protons</u> is <u>helium</u>.

If a substance only contains atoms with the <u>same number</u> of <u>protons</u> it's called an <u>element</u>.

So <u>all the atoms</u> of a particular <u>element</u> (e.g. nitrogen) have the <u>same number</u> of protons and <u>different elements</u> have atoms with <u>different numbers</u> of protons.

There are about <u>100 different elements</u>. Each element consists of only one type of atom — see diagram below.

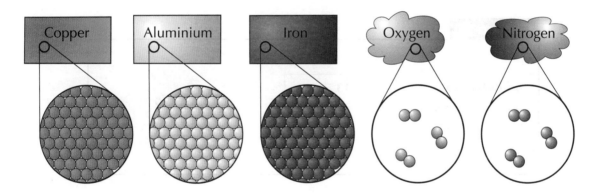

## Atoms Can be Represented by Symbols

1) Atoms of each element can be represented by a <u>one or two letter symbol</u> — it's a type of <u>shorthand</u> that saves you the bother of having to write the full name of the element.

2) Some make <u>perfect sense</u>, e.g.

C = carbon   O = oxygen   Mg = magnesium

3) Others less so, e.g.

Na = sodium   Fe = iron   Pb = lead

*Most of these odd symbols actually come from the Latin names of the elements.*

4) You'll see these symbols on the periodic table (see page 35).

---

## All atoms in an element have the same number of protons

<u>Atoms</u> and <u>elements</u> — make sure you know what they are and the <u>differences</u> between them. You don't need to learn all the symbols as you can use a <u>periodic table</u> but it's handy to know the common ones.

# Isotopes

What's inside different atoms of the <u>same element</u> can vary.  Read on to find out how...

## Isotopes are the Same Except for Extra **Neutrons**

1) <u>Isotopes</u> are defined as:

> <u>Different forms</u> of the <u>same element</u>, which have the
> <u>SAME number of PROTONS</u> but a <u>DIFFERENT number of NEUTRONS</u>.

2) So isotopes have the <u>same atomic number</u> but <u>different mass numbers</u>.

3) A very popular example of a pair of isotopes are <u>carbon-12</u> and <u>carbon-13</u>.

**Carbon-12**

6 PROTONS
6 ELECTRONS
6 NEUTRONS

$^{12}_{6}\text{C}$

**Carbon-13**

6 PROTONS
6 ELECTRONS
7 NEUTRONS

$^{13}_{6}\text{C}$

4) Because many elements can exist as a number of different isotopes, relative atomic mass
($A_r$) is used instead of mass number when referring to the element as a whole.

> <u>Relative atomic mass</u> is an <u>average</u> mass taking into account the different
> <u>masses and abundances</u> (amounts) of <u>all the isotopes</u> that make up the element.

5) You can use this formula to work out the relative atomic mass of an element:

$$\text{relative atomic mass } (A_r) = \frac{\text{sum of (isotope abundance} \times \text{isotope mass number)}}{\text{sum of abundances of all the isotopes}}$$

**EXAMPLE:** Copper has two stable isotopes.  Cu-63 has an abundance of 69.2% and Cu-65 has an
abundance of 30.8%.  Calculate the relative atomic mass of copper to 1 decimal place.

$$\text{Relative atomic mass} = \frac{(69.2 \times 63) + (30.8 \times 65)}{69.2 + 30.8} = \frac{4359.6 + 2002}{100} = \frac{6361.6}{100} = 63.616 = 63.6$$

# Compounds

It would be great if we only had to deal with elements. But unluckily for you, elements can mix and match to make lots of new substances called <u>compounds</u>. And this makes things a little bit more complicated...

## Atoms **Join Together** to Make **Compounds**

1) When <u>elements react</u>, atoms <u>combine</u> with other atoms to form <u>compounds</u>.

2) Compounds are substances formed from <u>two or more</u> elements, the atoms of each are in <u>fixed proportions</u> throughout the compound and they're held together by <u>chemical bonds</u>.

3) <u>Making bonds</u> involves atoms giving away, taking or sharing <u>electrons</u>. Only the <u>electrons</u> are involved — the nuclei of the atoms aren't affected at all when a bond is made.

4) It's <u>usually difficult</u> to <u>separate</u> the original elements of a compound out again — a chemical reaction is needed to do this.

   During a chemical reaction, at least one new substance is made. You can usually measure a change in energy, such as a temperature change, as well.

5) A compound which is formed from a <u>metal</u> and a <u>non-metal</u> consists of <u>ions</u>. The <u>metal</u> atoms <u>lose</u> electrons to form <u>positive ions</u> and the non-metal atoms <u>gain</u> electrons to form <u>negative ions</u>. The <u>opposite charges</u> (positive and negative) of the ions mean that they're strongly <u>attracted</u> to each other. This is called <u>ionic bonding</u>. Examples of compounds which are bonded ionically include sodium chloride, magnesium oxide and calcium oxide.

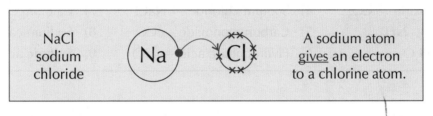

NaCl
sodium
chloride

A sodium atom
<u>gives</u> an electron
to a chlorine atom.

6) A compound formed from <u>non-metals</u> consists of <u>molecules</u>. Each atom <u>shares</u> an <u>electron</u> with another atom — this is called <u>covalent bonding</u>. Examples of compounds that are bonded covalently include hydrogen chloride gas, carbon monoxide, and water.

HCl
hydrogen
chloride

A hydrogen atom bonds
with a chlorine atom by
<u>sharing</u> an electron with it.

7) The <u>properties</u> of a compound are usually <u>totally different</u> from the properties of the <u>original elements</u>.

For example, if iron (a lustrous magnetic metal) and sulfur (a nice yellow powder) react, the compound formed (<u>iron sulfide</u>) is a <u>dull grey solid</u> lump, and doesn't behave <u>anything like</u> either iron or sulfur.

Mixture     Compound

# Formulas and Equations

Formulas and equations are used to show what is happening to substances involved in chemical reactions. They tell us what atoms are involved and how the substances change during a reaction.

## A Formula Shows What Atoms are in a Compound

Just as elements can be represented by symbols, compounds can be represented by formulas. The formulas are made up of elemental symbols in the same proportions that the elements can be found in the compound.

1) For example, carbon dioxide, $CO_2$, is a compound formed from a chemical reaction between carbon and oxygen. It contains 1 carbon atom and 2 oxygen atoms.

Carbon + Oxygen $\longrightarrow$ Carbon Dioxide

2) Here's another example: the formula of sulfuric acid is $H_2SO_4$. So, each molecule contains 2 hydrogen atoms, 1 sulfur atom and 4 oxygen atoms.

C + OO $\longrightarrow$ OCO $CO_2$

Elemental oxygen goes around in pairs of atoms (so it's $O_2$).

3) There might be brackets in a formula, e.g. calcium hydroxide is $Ca(OH)_2$. The little number outside the bracket applies to everything inside the brackets. So in $Ca(OH)_2$ there's 1 calcium atom, 2 oxygen atoms and 2 hydrogen atoms.

Here are some examples of formulas which might come in handy:

1) Carbon dioxide — $CO_2$
2) Ammonia — $NH_3$
3) Water — $H_2O$
4) Sodium chloride — $NaCl$
5) Carbon monoxide — $CO$
6) Hydrochloric acid — $HCl$
7) Calcium chloride — $CaCl_2$
8) Sodium carbonate — $Na_2CO_3$
9) Sulfuric acid — $H_2SO_4$

## Chemical Changes are Shown Using Chemical Equations

One way to show a chemical reaction is to write a word equation. It's not as quick as using chemical symbols and you can't tell straight away what's happened to each of the atoms, but it's dead easy.

Here's an example — you're told that methane burns in oxygen giving carbon dioxide and water:

methane + oxygen $\rightarrow$ carbon dioxide + water

The molecules on the left-hand side of the equation are called the reactants (because they react with each other).

The molecules on the right-hand side are called the products (because they've been produced from the reactants).

## Symbol Equations Show the Atoms on Both Sides

Chemical changes can be shown in a kind of shorthand using symbol equations. Symbol equations just show the symbols or formulas of the reactants and products...

magnesium + oxygen      magnesium oxide

$2Mg + O_2 \longrightarrow 2MgO$

You'll have spotted that there's a '2' in front of the Mg and the MgO. The reason for this is explained on the next page.

# Formulas and Equations

## Symbol Equations Need to be Balanced

1) There must always be the <u>same</u> number of atoms on <u>both sides</u> — they can't just <u>disappear</u>.

2) You <u>balance</u> the equation by putting numbers <u>in front</u> of the formulas where needed.

3) Take this equation for reacting sulfuric acid ($H_2SO_4$) with sodium hydroxide (NaOH) to get sodium sulfate ($Na_2SO_4$) and water ($H_2O$):

$$H_2SO_4 + NaOH \rightarrow Na_2SO_4 + H_2O$$

The <u>formulas</u> for all of the compounds are correct but the numbers of some atoms <u>don't match up</u> on both sides. E.g. there are 3 Hs on the left, but only 2 on the right. You <u>can't change formulas</u> like $H_2SO_4$ to $H_2SO_5$. You can only put numbers <u>in front of them</u>.

4) This equation needs <u>balancing</u> — see below for how to do this.

## Here's how to Balance an Equation

The more you <u>practise</u>, the <u>quicker</u> you get, but all you do is this:

1) Find an element that <u>doesn't balance</u> and <u>pencil in a number</u> to try and sort it out.

2) <u>See where it gets you</u>. It may create <u>another imbalance</u>, but if so, pencil in <u>another number</u> and see where that gets you.

3) Carry on chasing <u>unbalanced</u> elements and it'll <u>sort itself out</u> pretty quickly.

### EXAMPLE:

**In the equation above you soon notice we're short of H atoms on the RHS (Right-Hand Side).**

1) The only thing you can do about that is make it $2H_2O$ instead of just $H_2O$:

$$H_2SO_4 + NaOH \rightarrow Na_2SO_4 + 2H_2O$$

2) But that now causes too many H atoms and O atoms on the RHS, so to balance that up you could try putting 2NaOH on the LHS (Left-Hand Side):

$$H_2SO_4 + 2NaOH \rightarrow Na_2SO_4 + 2H_2O$$

3) And suddenly there it is! <u>Everything balances</u>. And you'll notice the Na just sorted itself out.

---

## Getting good at balancing equations takes patience and practice

Remember, a number <u>in front</u> of a formula applies to the <u>entire formula</u> — so, $3Na_2SO_4$ means three lots of $Na_2SO_4$. The little numbers <u>within or at the end</u> of a formula only apply to the <u>atom</u> or <u>brackets</u> immediately before. So the 4 in $Na_2SO_4$ means there are 4 Os, but there's just 1 S, not 4.

# Warm-Up & Exam Questions

So, you reckon you know your elements from your compounds?... Have a go at these questions and see how you do. If you get stuck on something just flick back and give it another read through.

## Warm-Up Questions

1) What does the mass number tell you about an atom?
2) What is the definition of an element?
3) Describe what a compound is.
4) What does a compound formed from a metal and a non-metal consist of?
5) Balance this equation for the reaction of glucose ($C_6H_{12}O_6$) and oxygen:
   $$C_6H_{12}O_6 + O_2 \rightarrow CO_2 + H_2O$$

## Exam Questions

**1** This question is about atomic structure.

**1.1** Use your knowledge to complete **Table 1**.

**Table 1**

| Name of particle | Relative charge |
|---|---|
| Proton | ................ |
| Neutron | ................ |

*[2 marks]*

**1.2** Where are protons and neutrons found in an atom?

*[1 mark]*

**1.3** An atom has 8 electrons. How many protons does the atom have?

*[1 mark]*

**1.4** What is the relative mass of a proton?

*[1 mark]*

**2** **Table 2** gives some information about nitrogen.

**Table 2**

| Element | Number of protons | Mass number |
|---|---|---|
| nitrogen | 7 | 14 |

**2.1** How many neutrons does nitrogen have?

*[1 mark]*

**2.2** Describe how the information in **Table 2** can be used to work out the atomic number of nitrogen.

*[1 mark]*

**2.3** What is the chemical symbol for nitrogen?

*[1 mark]*

# Exam Questions

**3** Methane ($CH_4$) burns in oxygen to make carbon dioxide and water.

**3.1** State the names of the reactants in this reaction.

*[1 mark]*

**3.2** State the names of the products in this reaction.

*[1 mark]*

**3.3** Which molecule involved in the reaction is composed of only one element.

*[1 mark]*

**3.4** Complete and balance the symbol equation for the reaction below.

$$\text{.........}CH_4 \quad + \quad \text{.................} \quad \rightarrow \quad \text{.........}CO_2 \quad + \quad \text{.........}H_2O$$

*[2 marks]*

**4** Sulfuric acid reacts with ammonia to form ammonium sulfate, $(NH_4)_2SO_4$.

**4.1** Complete and balance the symbol equation below.

$$\text{.................} \quad + \quad \text{.................} \quad \rightarrow \quad (NH_4)_2SO_4$$

*[3 marks]*

**4.2** In the balanced equation, how many atoms are there in the reactants?

*[1 mark]*

**4.3** How many hydrogen atoms are present in ammonium sulfate?

*[1 mark]*

**5** Carbon has several isotopes. These include carbon-12 and carbon-13.  Details about the carbon-13 isotope are shown below.

$$^{13}_{6}C$$

**5.1** Explain what an isotope is.

*[3 marks]*

**5.2** Give the number of protons, neutrons and electrons that carbon-13 contains.

*[3 marks]*

**5.3** Details of element **X** are shown below.

$$^{13}_{7}X$$

Explain how you can tell that element **X** is not an isotope of carbon.

*[1 mark]*

**5.4** There are two isotopes of element **X**. One isotope has a mass number of 13 and a percentage abundance of 79%. The other isotope has a mass number of 14 and a percentage abundance of 21%. Use this information to calculate the relative atomic mass of element **X**. Give your answer to 1 d.p.

*[4 marks]*

Topic 1 — Atomic Structure and the Periodic Table

# Mixtures

Mixtures are exactly what they sound like, two or more elements or compounds mixed together.

## Mixtures are Easily Separated — Not Like Compounds

1) Unlike in a compound, there's no chemical bond between the different parts of a mixture.

2) The parts of a mixture can be either elements or compounds, and they can be separated out by physical methods such as filtration (p. 26), crystallisation (p.26), simple distillation (p.28), fractional distillation (p.29) and chromatography (see next page).

*A physical method is one that doesn't involve a chemical reaction, so doesn't form any new substances.*

Air is a mixture of gases, mainly nitrogen, oxygen, carbon dioxide and argon.
The gases can all be separated out fairly easily.

Crude oil is a mixture of different length hydrocarbon molecules.

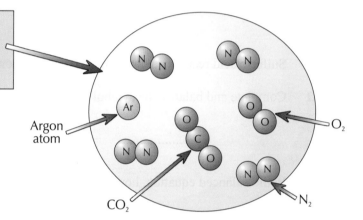

Argon atom

$CO_2$

$O_2$

$N_2$

3) The properties of a mixture are just a mixture of the properties of the separate parts — the chemical properties of a substance aren't affected by it being part of a mixture.

For example, a mixture of iron powder and sulfur powder will show the properties of both iron and sulfur. It will contain grey magnetic bits of iron and bright yellow bits of sulfur.

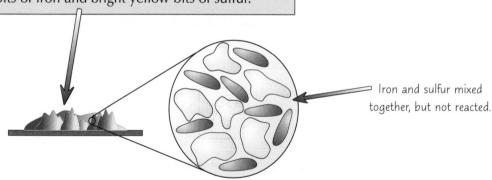

Iron and sulfur mixed together, but not reacted.

## Mixtures can be separated without a chemical reaction

Remember that the different parts of mixtures aren't chemically combined, this means their chemical properties remain unchanged and the compounds or elements can be separated by physical methods.

# Chromatography

Paper chromatography is a really useful technique to separate compounds out of a mixture.

## You Need to Know How to Do **Paper Chromatography**

One method of separating substances in a mixture is through chromatography.
This technique can be used to separate different dyes in an ink. Here's how you can do it:

1) Draw a line near the bottom of a sheet of filter paper.
(Use a pencil to do this — pencil marks are insoluble and won't dissolve in the solvent.)

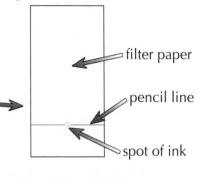

filter paper

pencil line

spot of ink

2) Add a spot of the ink to the line and place the sheet in a beaker of solvent, e.g. water.

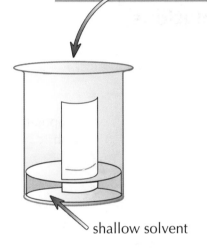

shallow solvent

3) The solvent used depends on what's being tested. Some compounds dissolve well in water, but sometimes other solvents, like ethanol, are needed.

4) Make sure the ink isn't touching the solvent — you don't want it to dissolve into it.

5) Place a lid on top of the container to stop the solvent evaporating.

6) The solvent seeps up the paper, carrying the ink with it.

The point the solvent has reached as it moves up the paper is the solvent front.

7) Each different dye in the ink will move up the paper at a different rate so the dyes will separate out. Each dye will form a spot in a different place — 1 spot per dye in the ink.

8) If any of the dyes in the ink are insoluble (won't dissolve) in the solvent you've used, they'll stay on the baseline.

9) When the solvent has nearly reached the top of the paper, take the paper out of the beaker and leave it to dry.

10) The end result is a pattern of spots called a chromatogram.

A chromatogram

## Chromatography separates the different dyes in inks

PRACTICAL TIP

Make sure you use a pencil to draw your baseline on the sheet of paper for your chromatogram. If you use a pen, all the components of the ink in the pen will get separated, along with the substance you're analysing, which will make your results very confusing.

#  Filtration and Crystallisation

Filtration and crystallisation are methods of separating mixtures. Chemists use these techniques all the time to separate solids from liquids, so it's worth making sure you know how to do them.

## Filtration Separates Insoluble Solids from Liquids

1) Filtration can be used if your product is an insoluble solid that needs to be separated from a liquid reaction mixture.

2) It can be used in purification as well. For example, solid impurities in the reaction mixture can be separated out using filtration.

Filter paper folded into a cone shape — the solid is left in the filter paper.

Insoluble means the solid can't be dissolved in the liquid.

## Two Ways to Separate Soluble Solids from Solutions

If a solid can be dissolved it's described as being soluble. There are two methods you can use to separate a soluble salt from a solution — evaporation and crystallisation.

### Evaporation

1) Pour the solution into an evaporating dish.

2) Slowly heat the solution. The solvent will evaporate and the solution will get more concentrated. Eventually, crystals will start to form.

3) Keep heating the evaporating dish until all you have left are dry crystals.

evaporating dish

You don't have to use a Bunsen burner, you could use a water bath, or an electric heater.

Evaporation is a really quick way of separating a soluble salt from a solution, but you can only use it if the salt doesn't decompose (break down) when its heated. Otherwise, you'll have to use crystallisation.

### Crystallisation

1) Pour the solution into an evaporating dish and gently heat the solution. Some of the solvent will evaporate and the solution will get more concentrated.

2) Once some of the solvent has evaporated, or when you see crystals start to form (the point of crystallisation), remove the dish from the heat and leave the solution to cool.

3) The salt should start to form crystals as it becomes insoluble in the cold, highly concentrated solution.

4) Filter the crystals out of the solution, and leave them in a warm place to dry. You could also use a drying oven or a dessicator.

You should also use crystallisation if you want to make nice big crystals of your salt.

Salt crystallising out of solution.

# Filtration and Crystallisation

Here's how you can put filtration and crystallisation to <u>good use</u>.  Separating rock salt...

## Filtration and Crystallisation can be Used to Separate Rock Salt

1) <u>Rock salt</u> is simply a <u>mixture</u> of <u>salt</u> and <u>sand</u> (they spread it on the roads in winter).
2) Salt and sand are both <u>compounds</u> — but <u>salt dissolves</u> in water and <u>sand doesn't</u>.
   This <u>vital difference</u> in their <u>physical properties</u> gives a great way to <u>separate</u> them.
   Here's what to do...

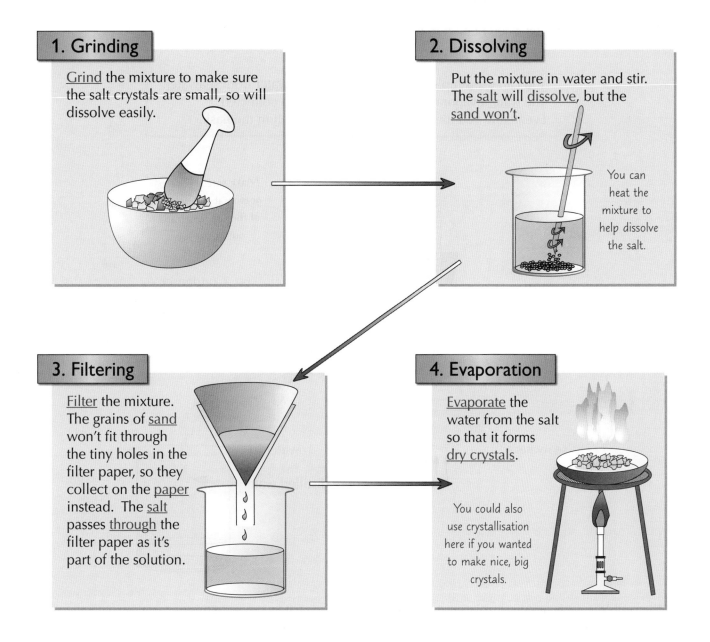

### 1. Grinding

<u>Grind</u> the mixture to make sure the salt crystals are small, so will dissolve easily.

### 2. Dissolving

Put the mixture in water and stir. The <u>salt</u> will <u>dissolve</u>, but the <u>sand won't</u>.

You can heat the mixture to help dissolve the salt.

### 3. Filtering

<u>Filter</u> the mixture. The grains of <u>sand</u> won't fit through the tiny holes in the filter paper, so they collect on the <u>paper</u> instead. The <u>salt</u> passes <u>through</u> the filter paper as it's part of the solution.

### 4. Evaporation

<u>Evaporate</u> the water from the salt so that it forms <u>dry crystals</u>.

You could also use crystallisation here if you wanted to make nice, big crystals.

---

## Separating rock salt requires filtration and evaporation

You may be asked how to separate <u>another type of mixture</u> containing <u>insoluble</u> and <u>soluble</u> solids — just apply the <u>same method</u> and <u>think through</u> what is happening in each stage.

**Distillation**

Distillation is used to separate mixtures which contain <u>liquids</u>. This first page looks at <u>simple</u> distillation.

## Simple Distillation is Used to **Separate Out Solutions**

1) <u>Simple distillation</u> is used for separating out a <u>liquid</u> from a <u>solution</u>.

2) The solution is <u>heated</u>. The part of the solution that has the lowest boiling point <u>evaporates</u> first.

3) The <u>vapour</u> is then <u>cooled</u>, <u>condenses</u> (turns back into a liquid) and is <u>collected</u>.

4) The rest of the <u>solution</u> is left behind in the flask.

You can use simple distillation to get <u>pure water</u> from <u>seawater</u>. The <u>water</u> evaporates and is condensed and collected. Eventually you'll end up with just the <u>salt</u> left in the flask.

5) The <u>problem</u> with simple distillation is that you can only use it to separate things with <u>very different</u> boiling points — if the temperature goes higher than the boiling point of the substance with the higher boiling point, they will <u>mix</u> again.

6) If you have a <u>mixture of liquids</u> with <u>similar boiling points</u> you need another method to separate them — like fractional distillation (see next page).

## Heating → Evaporating → Cooling → Condensing

You might have used <u>distilled water</u> in chemistry experiments. Because it's been distilled, there <u>aren't</u> any <u>impurities</u> in it (like ions, see page 46) that might interfere with experimental results. Clever stuff.

# Distillation

Another type of distillation is <u>fractional distillation</u>. This is more complicated to carry out than simple distillation but it can separate out <u>mixtures of liquids</u> even if their <u>boiling points</u> are close together.

## Fractional Distillation is Used to Separate a Mixture of Liquids

Here is a lab demonstration that can be used to model the <u>fractional distillation of crude oil</u> at a <u>refinery</u>.

thermometer

water out

condenser

coolest bit of column

fractionating column filled with glass rods

water in

hottest bit of column

crude oil substitute

*For safety reasons this experiment uses a substitute for real crude oil.*

heat

fractions collected at lower temperatures

1) You put your <u>mixture</u> in a flask and stick a <u>fractionating column</u> on top. Then you heat it.

2) The <u>different liquids</u> will all have <u>different boiling points</u> — so they will evaporate at <u>different temperatures</u>.

3) The liquid with the <u>lowest boiling point</u> evaporates first. When the temperature on the thermometer matches the boiling point of this liquid, it will reach the <u>top</u> of the column.

4) Liquids with <u>higher boiling points</u> might also start to evaporate. But the column is <u>cooler</u> towards the <u>top</u>. So they will only get part of the way up before <u>condensing</u> and running back down towards the flask.

5) When the first liquid has been collected, you <u>raise the temperature</u> until the <u>next one</u> reaches the top.

## Fractional distillation is used in the lab and industry

You've made it to the end of the pages on <u>separation techniques</u>, so make sure you understand what each of the methods can be used to separate and the <u>apparatus</u> set up for each technique.

# PRACTICAL Warm-Up & Exam Questions

So the last few pages have all been about mixtures and how to separate them. Here are some questions to get stuck into and make sure you know your filtration from your distillation...

## Warm-Up Questions

1) What is the definition of a mixture?
2) Name a separation technique that could be used to separate a soluble solid from a solution.
3) Which technique could you use to separate a mixture of liquids with similar boiling points?

## Exam Questions

1 A forensic scientist is using paper chromatography to compare different inks which contain a mixture of dyes. He draws a pencil line near the bottom of a sheet of filter paper and adds a spot of each of the different inks to the line with a gap between each spot.

1.1 Describe the next step that's required to carry out paper chromatography.

*[1 mark]*

1.2 Why is pencil used to make the line on the filter paper?

*[1 mark]*

2 Lawn sand is a mixture of insoluble sharp sand and soluble ammonium sulfate fertiliser.

2.1 Describe how you would obtain pure, dry samples of the two components of lawn sand in the lab.

*[3 marks]*

2.2 A student separated 51.4 g of lawn sand into sharp sand and ammonium sulfate. After separation, the total mass of the two products was 52.6 g. Suggest a reason for the difference in mass.

*[1 mark]*

3 **Table 1** gives the boiling points of three liquids.

3.1 State why simple distillation cannot be used to separate water from a solution of water and methanoic acid.

*[1 mark]*

**Table 1**

| Liquid | Boiling point (°C) |
|---|---|
| Methanoic acid | 101 |
| Propanone | 56 |
| Water | 100 |

**Figure 1**

3.2 The apparatus in **Figure 1** was used to separate a mixture of propanone and water.

Complete the table using the options below.

**no liquid      water      propanone      both liquids**

| Temperature on thermometer | Contents of the flask | Contents of the beaker |
|---|---|---|
| 30 °C | ............. | ............. |
| 65 °C | ............. | ............. |
| 110 °C | ............. | ............. |

*[3 marks]*

# The History of the Atom

You may have thought you were done with the atom after page 16.  Unfortunately, you don't get away that easily.  The next couple of pages are all about how scientists came to understand the atom as we do today.

## The Theory of Atomic Structure Has Changed Over Time

1) At the start of the 19th century John Dalton described atoms as solid spheres, and said that different spheres made up the different elements.

2) In 1897 J J Thomson concluded from his experiments that atoms weren't solid spheres.  His measurements of charge and mass showed that an atom must contain even smaller, negatively charged particles — electrons.

3) The 'solid sphere' idea of atomic structure had to be changed.  The new theory was known as the 'plum pudding model'.

4) The plum pudding model showed the atom as a ball of positive charge with electrons stuck in it.

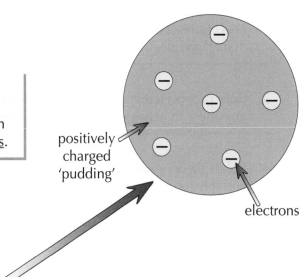

positively charged 'pudding'

electrons

## Rutherford Showed that the Plum Pudding Model Was Wrong

1) In 1909 Ernest Rutherford and his student Ernest Marsden conducted the famous alpha particle scattering experiments.  They fired positively charged alpha particles at an extremely thin sheet of gold.

2) From the plum pudding model, they were expecting the particles to pass straight through the sheet or be slightly deflected at most.  This was because the positive charge of each atom was thought to be very spread out through the 'pudding' of the atom.  But, whilst most of the particles did go straight through the gold sheet, some were deflected more than expected, and a small number were deflected backwards.  So the plum pudding model couldn't be right.

3) Rutherford came up with an idea to explain this new evidence — the nuclear model of the atom.  In this, there's a tiny, positively charged nucleus at the centre, where most of the mass is concentrated.  A 'cloud' of negative electrons surrounds this nucleus — so most of the atom is empty space.  When alpha particles came near the concentrated, positive charge of the nucleus, they were deflected.  If they were fired directly at the nucleus, they were deflected backwards.  Otherwise, they passed through the empty space.

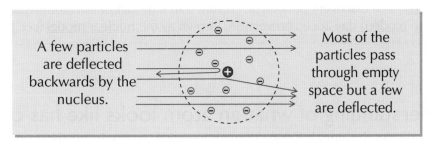

A few particles are deflected backwards by the nucleus.

Most of the particles pass through empty space but a few are deflected.

# The History of the Atom

## Bohr's **Nuclear Model** Explains a Lot

1) Scientists realised that electrons in a 'cloud' around the nucleus of an atom, as Rutherford described, would be attracted to the nucleus, causing the atom to <u>collapse</u>.

2) Niels Bohr's nuclear model of the atom suggested that all the electrons were contained in <u>shells</u>.

3) Bohr proposed that electrons <u>orbit</u> the nucleus in <u>fixed shells</u> and aren't anywhere in between. Each shell is a fixed distance from the nucleus.

4) Bohr's theory of atomic structure was supported by many <u>experiments</u> and it helped to explain lots of other scientists' <u>observations</u> at the time.

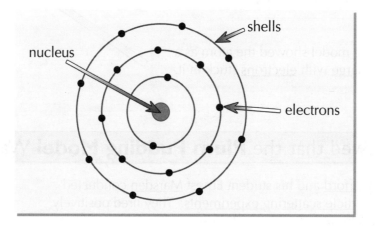

## Further Experiments Showed the **Existence** of **Protons**

1) Further experimentation by Rutherford and others gave the conclusion that the nucleus could be <u>divided</u> into smaller particles, each of which has the <u>same charge</u> as a <u>hydrogen nucleus</u>.

2) About 20 years after scientists had accepted that atoms have nuclei, <u>James Chadwick</u> carried out an experiment which provided evidence for <u>neutral particles</u> in the nucleus. These became known as <u>neutrons</u>. The discovery of neutrons resulted in a model of the atom which was <u>pretty close</u> to the <u>modern day</u> accepted version, known as the <u>nuclear model</u> (see page 16).

## Our understanding of what an atom looks like has changed

Our understanding of the atom has gone through <u>many stages</u> thanks to other people's work being built upon with <u>new evidence</u> and <u>new predictions</u> made. A fine example of the scientific method.

# Electronic Structure

The fact that electrons occupy 'shells' around the nucleus is what causes the whole of chemistry. Remember that, and watch how it applies to each bit of it.

## Electron Shell **Rules:**

1) Electrons always occupy <u>shells</u> (sometimes called <u>energy levels</u>).

2) The <u>lowest</u> energy levels are <u>always filled first</u> — these are the ones closest to the nucleus.

3) Only <u>a certain number</u> of electrons are allowed in each shell:

> 1st shell: 2    2nd shell: 8    3rd shell: 8

4) Atoms are much <u>happier</u> when they have <u>full electron shells</u> — like the <u>noble gases</u> in <u>Group 0</u>.

5) In most atoms, the <u>outer shell</u> is <u>not full</u> and this makes the atom want to <u>react</u> to fill it.

Electron configurations can be shown as <u>diagrams</u> like this...

3rd shell still filling

...or as <u>numbers</u> like this: 2, 8, 1
Both of the configurations above are for <u>sodium</u>.

## Follow the Rules to **Work Out** Electronic Structures

You can easily work out the <u>electronic structures</u> for the first <u>20</u> elements of the periodic table (things get a bit more complicated after that).

**EXAMPLE:**

**What is the electronic structure of nitrogen?**

1) Nitrogen's atomic number is 7. This means it has 7 protons... so it must have 7 electrons.

2) Follow the 'Electron Shell Rules' above. The first shell can only take 2 electrons and the second shell can take a maximum of 8 electrons.

So the electronic structure for nitrogen must be 2, 5.

**EXAMPLE:**

**What is the electronic structure of magnesium?**

1) Magnesium's atomic number is 12. This means it has 12 protons... so it must have 12 electrons.

2) Follow the 'Electron Shell Rules' above. The first shell can only take 2 electrons and the second shell can take a maximum of 8 electrons, so the third shell must also be partially filled.

So the electronic structure for magnesium must be 2, 8, 2.

Here are some more examples of electronic structures:

H Hydrogen

1
Proton no. = 1

He Helium

2
Proton no. = 2

Li Lithium

2,1
Proton no. = 3

C Carbon

2,4
Proton no. = 6

Ne Neon

2,8
Proton no. = 10

Ca Calcium

2,8,8,2
Proton no. = 20

---

# Electron shells — one of the most important ideas in chemistry

It's <u>really important</u> to learn the rules for filling <u>electron shells</u> — make sure you practise.

# Development of the Periodic Table

We haven't always known as much about chemistry as we do now. Early chemists looked to try and understand <u>patterns</u> in the elements' properties to get a bit of understanding.

## In the **Early 1800s** Elements Were **Arranged** By **Atomic Mass**

Until quite recently, there were <u>two</u> obvious ways to categorise elements:

> 1) Their <u>physical</u> and <u>chemical properties</u>    2) Their <u>relative atomic mass</u>

1) Remember, scientists had <u>no idea</u> of <u>atomic structure</u> or of <u>protons</u>, neutrons or <u>electrons</u>, so there was no such thing as <u>atomic number</u> to them. (It was only in the 20th century after protons and electrons were discovered that it was realised the elements were best arranged in order of <u>atomic number</u>.)

> Remember — the relative atomic mass is the average mass of one atom of an element.

2) <u>Back then</u>, the only thing they could measure was <u>relative atomic mass</u>, and so the <u>known</u> elements were arranged <u>in order of atomic mass</u>. When this was done, a <u>periodic pattern</u> was noticed in the <u>properties</u> of the elements. This is where the name '<u>periodic table</u>' comes from...

3) Early periodic tables were not complete and some elements were placed in the <u>wrong group</u>. This is because <u>elements</u> were placed in the <u>order of relative atomic mass</u> and did not take into account their properties.

## **Dmitri Mendeleev** Left Gaps and **Predicted** New Elements

1) In <u>1869</u>, <u>Dmitri Mendeleev</u> overcame some of the problems of early periodic tables by taking 50 known elements and arranging them into his Table of Elements — with various <u>gaps</u> as shown.

### Mendeleev's Table of the Elements

```
H
Li Be                                          B  C  N  O  F
Na Mg                                          Al Si P  S  Cl
K  Ca *  Ti V  Cr Mn Fe Co Ni Cu Zn *  *  As Se Br
Rb Sr Y  Zr Nb Mo *  Ru Rh Pd Ag Cd In Sn Sb Te I
Cs Ba *  *  Ta W  *  Os Ir Pt Au Hg Tl Pb Bi
```

2) Mendeleev put the elements <u>mainly</u> in order of <u>atomic mass</u> but did switch that order if the properties meant it should be changed. An example of this can been seen with <u>Te</u> and <u>I</u> — iodine actually has a <u>smaller</u> relative atomic mass but is placed after tellurium as it has <u>similar properties</u> to the elements in that group.

3) <u>Gaps</u> were left in the table to make sure that elements with similar properties stayed in the same groups. Some of these <u>gaps</u> indicated the existence of undiscovered elements and allowed Mendeleev to predict what their properties might be. When they were found and they <u>fitted the pattern</u> it helped confirm Mendeleev's ideas. For example, Mendeleev made really good predictions about the chemical and physical properties of an element he called <u>ekasilicon</u>, which we know today as <u>germanium</u>.

> The discovery of <u>isotopes</u> (see page 18) in the early 20th century confirmed that Mendeleev was correct to <u>not</u> place elements in a <u>strict order</u> of atomic mass but to also take account of their <u>properties</u>. Isotopes of the same element have <u>different atomic masses</u> but have the same <u>chemical properties</u> so occupy the same position on the periodic table.

## By leaving gaps in the table Mendeleev had the right idea

Make sure you can <u>describe</u> what Mendeleev did to <u>overcome problems</u> with early periodic tables.

# The Modern Periodic Table

Chemists were getting pretty close to producing something that you might <u>recognise</u> as a periodic table. The big breakthrough came when the <u>structure</u> of the <u>atom</u> was understood a bit better.

## The Periodic Table Helps you to **See Patterns** in **Properties**

1) There are <u>100ish elements</u>, which all materials are made of.

2) In the periodic table the elements are laid out in order of <u>increasing atomic (proton) number</u>. Arranging the elements like this means there are <u>repeating patterns</u> in the <u>properties</u> of the elements (the properties are said to occur periodically, hence the name periodic table).

3) If it wasn't for the periodic table <u>organising everything</u>, you'd have a <u>hard job</u> remembering all those properties.

4) It's a handy tool for working out which elements are <u>metals</u> and which are <u>non-metals</u>. Metals are found to the <u>left</u> and non-metals to the <u>right</u>.

alkali metals (see page 38-39)

halogens (see page 40-41)

noble gases (see page 42)

(pink line separates metals and non-metals)

5) Elements with <u>similar properties</u> form <u>columns</u>.

6) These <u>vertical columns</u> are called <u>groups</u>.

7) The <u>group number</u> tells you how many <u>electrons</u> there are in the <u>outer shell</u>. For example, <u>Group 1</u> elements all have <u>one</u> electron in their outer shell and <u>Group 7</u> all have <u>seven</u> electrons in their outer shell. The exception to the rule is <u>Group 0</u>, for example helium has two electrons in its outer shell. This is useful as the way atoms react depends upon <u>the number of electrons</u> in their <u>outer shell</u>. So all elements in the same group are likely to react in a similar way.

8) If you know the <u>properties</u> of <u>one element</u>, you can <u>predict</u> properties of <u>other elements</u> in that group — and in the exam, you might be asked to do this. For example the <u>Group 1</u> elements are Li, Na, K, Rb, Cs and Fr. They're all <u>metals</u> and they <u>react in a similar way</u> (see pages 34-39).

9) You can also make predictions about trends in <u>reactivity</u>. E.g. in Group 1, the elements react <u>more vigorously</u> as you go <u>down</u> the group. And in Group 7, <u>reactivity decreases</u> as you go down the group.

10) The <u>rows</u> are called <u>periods</u>. Each new period represents another <u>full shell</u> of electrons.

## The modern periodic table is vital for understanding chemistry

This is a good example of how science progresses. A scientist has a <u>basically good</u> (though incomplete) <u>hypothesis</u> (see page 1), other scientists <u>question it</u> and <u>bring more evidence</u> to the table. The hypothesis may be <u>modified</u> or even <u>scrapped</u> to take account of available evidence. Only when all of the available evidence <u>supports</u> a hypothesis will it be <u>accepted</u>.

# Warm-Up & Exam Questions

The last few pages have been tough with lots of information to learn. Luckily, here are some questions to get your head around to help you test your understanding.

## Warm-Up Questions

1) Describe J J Thomson's model of the atom.
2) How many electrons can be held in the following:
   a) the first shell of an atom?
   b) the second shell of an atom?
3) What discovery supported Mendeleev's decision not to place elements in order of relative atomic mass?

## Exam Questions

**1**  Sodium has an atomic number of 11.

**1.1**  Complete the dot and cross diagram to show the electron configuration of sodium.

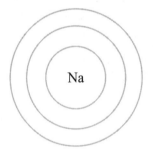

Na

*[1 mark]*

**1.2**  Sodium is in Group 1.
Name another element that would have the same number of outer shell electrons.

*[1 mark]*

**1.3**  How many electrons does sodium need to lose so that it has a full outer shell?

*[1 mark]*

**2**  The periodic table contains all the known elements arranged in order.

**2.1**  How were elements generally ordered in early periodic tables?

*[1 mark]*

**2.2**  How are the elements arranged in the modern periodic table?

*[1 mark]*

**2.3**  If two elements are in the same group of the periodic table what will they have in common?
Explain your answer.

*[1 mark]*

**3\***  Describe how the theory of atomic structure has changed throughout history.

*[6 marks]*

# Metals and Non-Metals

Metals are used for all sorts of things so they're <u>really important</u> in modern life.

## Most Elements are Metals

1) Metals are elements which can <u>form positive ions</u> when they react.
2) They're towards the <u>bottom</u> and to the <u>left</u> of the periodic table.
3) <u>Most elements</u> in the periodic table are metals.
4) <u>Non-metals</u> are at the far <u>right</u> and <u>top</u> of the periodic table.
5) Non-metals <u>don't</u> generally <u>form positive ions</u> when they react.

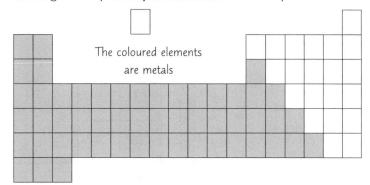

The coloured elements are metals

Only the white elements are non-metals.

## The Electronic Structure of Atoms Affects How They Will React

1) Atoms generally react to form a <u>full outer shell</u>. They do this via <u>losing</u>, <u>gaining</u> or <u>sharing</u> electrons.

2) Metals to the <u>left</u> of the periodic table <u>don't</u> have many <u>electrons to remove</u> and metals towards the <u>bottom</u> of the periodic table have outer electrons which are a <u>long way</u> from the nucleus so feel a weaker attraction. <u>Both</u> these effects mean that <u>not much energy</u> is needed to remove the electrons so it's <u>feasible</u> for the elements to react to <u>form positive ions</u> with a full outer shell.

3) For <u>non-metals</u>, forming positive ions is much <u>more difficult</u>. This is because they are either to the right of the periodic table — where they have <u>lots of electrons</u> to remove to get a full outer shell, or towards the top — where the outer electrons are close to the nucleus so feel a <u>strong attraction</u>. It's far more feasible for them to either <u>share</u> or <u>gain</u> electrons to get a full outer shell.

## Metals and Non-Metals Have Different Physical Properties

1) All metals have <u>metallic bonding</u> which causes them to have <u>similar</u> basic physical properties.

   • They're <u>strong</u> (hard to break), but can be <u>bent</u> or <u>hammered</u> into different shapes (malleable).
   • They're great at <u>conducting heat</u> and <u>electricity</u>.
   • They have <u>high boiling and melting points</u>.

2) As non-metals <u>don't</u> have metallic bonding, they don't tend to exhibit the same properties as metals. They tend to be <u>dull looking</u>, more <u>brittle</u>, <u>aren't always solids</u> at room temperature, <u>don't</u> generally <u>conduct electricity</u> and often have a <u>lower density</u>.

*Non-metals form a variety of different structures so have a wide range of chemical properties.*

## Metals have quite different properties from non-metals

So, all <u>metals</u> can conduct <u>electricity</u> and <u>heat</u> and be <u>bent</u> into shape, whereas mainly <u>non-metals</u> can't.

# Group 1 Elements

Group 1 elements are known as the <u>alkali metals</u> — these are silvery solids that have
to be stored in oil (and handled with forceps) as they're very reactive.

## The **Group 1** Elements are **Reactive**, **Soft** Metals

1) The alkali metals are lithium, sodium, potassium, rubidium, caesium and francium.
2) The alkali metals are all <u>soft</u> and have <u>low density</u>
   The <u>first three</u> in the group are <u>less dense than water</u>.
3) They all have <u>one electron</u> in their <u>outer shell</u>.  This makes
   them very reactive and gives them <u>similar properties</u>.

## **Trends** of Alkali Metals:

The trends for the alkali metals as
you go <u>down</u> Group 1 include:

1) <u>Increasing reactivity</u> — the outer electron is
   <u>more easily lost</u> as the attraction between
   the nucleus and electron decreases, because
   the electron is further away from the nucleus
   the further down the group you go.
2) <u>Lower melting and boiling points</u>.
3) <u>Higher relative atomic mass</u>.

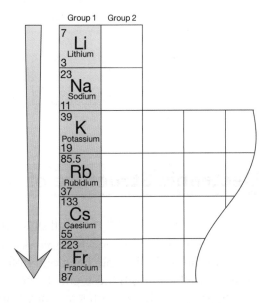

## Alkali Metals Form **Ionic Compounds** with **Non-Metals**

1) The Group 1 elements don't need much energy to lose their one outer
   electron to form a full outer shell, so they readily form <u>1+ ions</u>.

There's more on ionic
compounds on page 49.

2) It's so easy for them to lose their outer electron that they only ever react form ionic compounds.
   These compounds are usually <u>white solids</u> that dissolve in water to form <u>colourless solutions</u>.

*Details of the reactions of
Group 1 metals with non-metals
are on the next page.*

A <u>lithium</u> atom loses an
electron to become a +1 ion.

## The properties of Group 1 metals change as you go down the group

In the exam you might be given a <u>trend</u> and then asked to <u>predict properties</u> of other Group 1 metals.
For example, the <u>reactivity</u> of Group 1 metals <u>increases</u> as you go <u>down the group</u>,
so you know that potassium will react more vigorously than sodium.

Topic 1 — Atomic Structure and the Periodic Table

# Group 1 Elements

You met Group 1 metals on the previous page, so now it's time to learn about some of their reactions...

## Reactions of Alkali Metals with Non-Metals:

### Reaction with water

1) When Group 1 metals are put in water, they react vigorously to produce hydrogen gas and metal hydroxides — salts that dissolve in water to produce alkaline solutions.

$$2Na_{(s)} + 2H_2O_{(l)} \rightarrow 2NaOH_{(aq)} + H_{2(g)}$$
sodium + water → sodium hydroxide + hydrogen

All the Group 1 metals react with water in a similar way.

2) The more reactive (lower down in the group) an alkali metal is, the more violent the reaction.

3) The amount of energy given out by the reaction increases down the group — the reaction with potassium releases enough energy to ignite hydrogen.

### Reaction with chlorine

1) Group 1 metals react vigorously when heated in chlorine gas to form white metal chloride salts.

$$2Na_{(s)} + Cl_{2(g)} \rightarrow 2NaCl_{(s)}$$
sodium + chlorine → sodium chloride

2) As you go down the group, reactivity increases so the reaction with chlorine gets more vigorous.

### Reaction with oxygen

The Group 1 metals can react with oxygen to form a metal oxide. Different types of oxide will form depending on the Group 1 metal:

- Lithium reacts to form lithium oxide ($Li_2O$).
- Sodium reacts to form a mixture of sodium oxide ($Na_2O$) and sodium peroxide ($Na_2O_2$).
- Potassium reacts to form a mixture of potassium peroxide ($K_2O_2$) and potassium superoxide ($KO_2$).

The reactions with oxygen are why Group 1 metals tarnish in the air — the metal reacts with oxygen in the air to form a dull metal oxide layer.

## So now you know why they are called alkali metals...

...because they react with water to give alkaline solutions. Make sure you also know how they react with chlorine and oxygen. Memorise a couple of example equations for these reactions.

# Group 7 Elements

The Group 7 elements are known as the halogens.  Similarly to the alkali metals, halogens also show trends down the group.  However, these trends are a bit different...

## The **Halogens** are All **Non-Metals** with **Coloured Vapours**

- Fluorine is a very reactive, poisonous yellow gas.

- Chlorine is a fairly reactive, poisonous dense green gas.

- Bromine is a dense, poisonous, red-brown volatile liquid.

- Iodine is a dark grey crystalline solid or a purple vapour.

- They all exist as molecules which are pairs of atoms.

$F_2$    $Cl_2$    $Br_2$    $I_2$

## Learn These **Trends**:

As you go down Group 7, the halogens:

1) become less reactive — it's harder to gain an extra electron, because the outer shell's further from the nucleus.
2) have higher melting and boiling points.
3) have higher relative atomic masses.

All the Group 7 elements react in similar ways.  This is because they all have seven electrons in their outer shell.

You can use these trends to predict properties of halogens.
For example, you know that iodine will have a higher boiling point
than chlorine as it's further down the group in the periodic table.

## **Halogens** can Form **Molecular Compounds**

Halogen atoms can share electrons via covalent bonding (see page 52) with other non-metals so as to achieve a full outer shell.  For example HCl, $PCl_5$, HF and $CCl_4$ contain covalent bonds.
The compounds that form when halogens react with non-metals all have simple molecular structures.

## Halogens all exist as molecules with two atoms

Just like alkali metals, you may be asked to predict the properties of a halogen from a given trend down the group.  Make sure you understand why their electronic structure means halogens react in similar ways.

# Group 7 Elements

## Halogens Form **Ionic Bonds** with **Metals**

1) The halogens form <u>1– ions</u> called <u>halides</u> (F$^-$, Cl$^-$, Br$^-$ and I$^-$) when they bond with <u>metals</u>, for example  Na$^+$Cl$^-$  or  Fe$^{3+}$Br$^-_3$.

2) The compounds that form have <u>ionic structures</u>.

3) The diagram shows the bonding in sodium chloride, NaCl.

<u>Sodium</u> loses an electron and forms a +1 ion and <u>chlorine</u> gains an electron forming a –1 ion.

## More Reactive Halogens Will **Displace** Less Reactive Ones

A <u>displacement reaction</u> can occur between a more reactive halogen and the salt of a less reactive one.

For example, <u>chlorine</u> can displace <u>bromine</u> and <u>iodine</u> from an aqueous <u>solution</u> of its salt (a <u>bromide</u> or <u>iodide</u>).  <u>Bromine</u> will also displace <u>iodine</u> because of the <u>trend</u> in <u>reactivity</u>.

$$Cl_{2\,(g)} + 2KI_{(aq)} \rightarrow I_{2\,(aq)} + 2KCl_{(aq)}$$
Pale Green ............ Brown

$$Cl_{2\,(g)} + 2KBr_{(aq)} \rightarrow Br_{2\,(aq)} + 2KCl_{(aq)}$$
Pale Green ............ Orange

Cl$_2$ gas

Solution of potassium iodide

Iodine forming in solution

## Halogens all have different reactivities

Once more, you don't have to be a mind-reader to be able to guess the kind of thing they could ask you about halogens in the exam.  Something to do with displacement reactions seems very possible — will iodine displace bromine from some compound or other, for instance.  Make sure you learn the trends.

# Group 0 Elements

The <u>noble gases don't react</u> with very much and you can't even see them — makes them, a bit <u>dull</u> really.

## Group 0 Elements are All **Inert, Colourless Gases**

1) Group 0 elements are called the <u>noble gases</u> and include the elements <u>helium</u>, <u>neon</u> and <u>argon</u> (plus a few others).

2) They all have <u>eight electrons</u> in their outer energy level, apart from helium which has two, giving them a <u>full outer-shell</u>. As their outer shell is energetically stable they don't need to <u>give up</u> or <u>gain</u> electrons to become more stable. This means they are more or less <u>inert</u> — they <u>don't react</u> with much at all.

3) They exist as <u>monatomic gases</u> — single atoms <u>not</u> bonded to each other.

4) All elements in Group 0 are <u>colourless gases</u> at room temperature.

5) As the noble gases are inert they're <u>non-flammable</u> — they won't set on fire.

*Helium only has electrons in the first shell, which only needs 2 to be filled.*

## There are **Patterns** in the **Properties** of the Noble Gases

1) The <u>boiling points</u> of the noble gases <u>increase</u> as you move <u>down</u> the group along with increasing relative atomic mass.

2) The increase in boiling point is due to an <u>increase</u> in the <u>number of electrons</u> in each <u>atom</u> leading to <u>greater intermolecular forces</u> between them which need to be overcome. There's more on intermolecular forces for small molecules on page 54.

3) In the exam you may be given the boiling point of one noble gas and asked to <u>estimate</u> the value for <u>another one</u>. So make sure you know the <u>pattern</u>.

| Noble Gas |
| --- |
| helium |
| neon |
| argon |
| krypton |
| xenon |
| radon |

Increasing boiling point

 **EXAMPLE:**

**Neon is a gas at 25°C. Predict what state helium is at this temperature.**

Helium has a lower boiling than neon as it is further up the group.
So, helium must also be a gas at 25°C.

**EXAMPLE:**

**Radon and krypton have boiling points of –62 °C and –153 °C respectively. Predict the boiling point of xenon.**

Xenon comes in between radon and krypton in the group so you can predict that its boiling point would be halfway between their boiling points: $(-153) + (-62) = -215$

$$-215 \div 2 = -107.5 \approx -108°C$$

So, xenon should have a boiling point of about –108 °C

*The actual boiling point of xenon is –108 °C — just as predicted.*

## Just like other groups of elements, the noble gases follow patterns...

Although they're <u>unreactive</u> and <u>hard to see</u>, they're actually pretty useful. It took a while to discover them, but we now know all about them, including the trend in their boiling points.

# Warm-Up & Exam Questions

These questions are all about the groups of the periodic table that you need to know about. Treat the exam questions like the real thing — don't look back through the book until you've finished.

## Warm-Up Questions

1) What kind of ions do metals form?
2) Give three physical properties of most metals.
3) Which product is formed when lithium reacts with oxygen?
4) Do halide ions have a positive or a negative charge?
5) In which group of the periodic table are the noble gases?

## Exam Questions

**1** **Table 1** shows some of the physical properties of four of the halogens.

**Table 1**

| Halogen | Properties | | | |
|---|---|---|---|---|
| | **Atomic number** | **Colour** | **Physical state at room temperature** | **Reactivity** |
| Fluorine | 9 | yellow | gas | .............. |
| Chlorine | 17 | green | gas | .............. |
| Bromine | 35 | red-brown | liquid | .............. |
| Iodine | 53 | dark grey | solid | .............. |

**1.1** **Table 1** has a column for reactivity. Write an **X** in the row of the halogen with the **highest** reactivity and a **Y** in the row of the halogen with the **lowest** reactivity.

*[2 marks]*

**1.2** Which halogen in **Table 1** has the highest melting point?

*[1 mark]*

**2** **Figure 1** shows the periodic table.

**2.1** Element **X** is found in the first column of the periodic table. What name is given to the elements found in this part of the table?

*[1 mark]*

**2.2** Element **Y** does not conduct electricity. Predict whether element **Y** will be found to the left or the right of line **A** in **Figure 1**. Explain your answer.

*[2 marks]*

**Figure 1**

line **A**

X

# Exam Questions

**3**    Chlorine is a Group 7 element.
Its electron arrangement is shown in the diagram below.

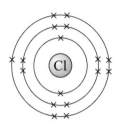

**3.1**    Chlorine is very reactive and forms compounds with metals.
What type of bonds form between chlorine and metals?

*[1 mark]*

When chlorine is bubbled through potassium iodide solution a reaction occurs.
The equation below shows the reaction.

$$Cl_{2(g)} + 2KI_{(aq)} \rightarrow I_{2(aq)} + 2KCl_{(aq)}$$

**3.2**    State what type of reaction this is.

*[1 mark]*

**3.3**    Which is the less reactive halogen in this reaction?  Explain your answer.

*[2 marks]*

**3.4**    Chlorine gas can also react with potassium bromide.
Using your knowledge of Group 7 elements predict the products of this reaction and their states.
Give an explanation for you answer.

*[4 marks]*

**3.5**    None of the elements in Group 0 will react with potassium iodide or potassium bromide.
Using your knowledge of the electronic structure of the Group 0 elements,
explain why no reaction occurs.

*[2 marks]*

**4**    Group 1 elements are metals.
They include lithium, sodium and potassium.

**4.1**    Explain why the Group 1 elements react vigorously with water.

*[1 mark]*

**4.2**    The Group 1 elements all react with water at a different rate.  Explain why this is.

*[3 marks]*

**4.3**    Give the two products formed when potassium reacts with water.

*[2 marks]*

**4.4**    During these reactions a solution is formed.
Is this solution acidic, neutral or alkaline?

*[1 marks]*

# Revision Summary for Topic 1

Well, that wraps up <u>Topic 1</u> — time to put yourself to the test and find out <u>how much you really know</u>.

- Try these questions and <u>tick off each one</u> when you <u>get it right</u>.
- When you've done <u>all the questions</u> under a heading and are <u>completely happy</u> with it, tick it off.

## Atomic Structure, Compounds and Formulas (p.16-21) ☐

1) Sketch an atom. Label the nucleus and the electrons.
2) What is the relative mass of a neutron?
3) True or false? Elements only contain atoms with the same number of protons.
4) Define relative atomic mass.
5) How similar are the properties of a compound to the elements that it's made from?
6) Give the formula for:
   a) carbon dioxide   b) sodium carbonate   c) hydrochloric acid
7) Balance these equations:
   a) $Mg + O_2 \rightarrow MgO$   b) $H_2SO_4 + NaOH \rightarrow Na_2SO_4 + H_2O$

## Mixtures and Separation (p.24-29) ☐

8) What is the difference between a compound and a mixture?
9) What is the name of the pattern of spots generated by paper chromatography?
10) Give the name of a method used to separate an insoluble solid from a liquid.
11) Describe how different substances are separated by fractional distillation.

## Atomic Structure and the History of the Periodic Table (p.31-35) ☑

12) Who demonstrated that the plum pudding model was wrong?
13) What did Bohr's nuclear model of the atom suggest?
14) Give the electronic structure of the following elements as numbers:
    a) helium   b) carbon   c) sodium
15) Why did Mendeleev leave gaps in his Table of Elements?
16) What name is given to the vertical columns in the periodic table?
17) How are the group number and the number of electrons in the outer shell of an element related?

## Groups of the Periodic Table (p.37-42) ☑

18) Where are non-metals on the periodic table?
19) State three trends in Group 1 elements as you go down the group.
20) State the products of the reaction of sodium and water.
21) How do the boiling points of halogens change as you go down the group?
22) How many atoms are in each molecule of a halogen?
23) What is the charge of the ions that halogens form when they react with metals?
24) What is the trend in boiling point as you go down Group 0?

# Ions

Ions crop up all over the place in chemistry. You're gonna have to be able to explain <u>how</u> they form and predict the <u>charges</u> of simple ions formed by elements in Groups 1, 2, 6 and 7.

## Ions are Made When **Electrons** are Transferred

1) <u>Ions</u> are <u>charged</u> particles — they can be <u>single atoms</u> (e.g. Cl⁻) or <u>groups of atoms</u> (e.g. $NO_3^-$).

2) When <u>atoms</u> lose or gain electrons to form ions, all they're trying to do is get a <u>full outer shell</u> like a <u>noble gas</u> (also called a "<u>stable electronic structure</u>"). Atoms with full outer shells are very <u>stable</u>.

   *Remember that the noble gases are in Group O of the periodic table.*

3) When <u>metals</u> form ions, they <u>lose</u> electrons from their <u>outer shell</u> to form <u>positive ions</u>.

4) When <u>non-metals</u> form ions, they <u>gain</u> electrons into their <u>outer shell</u> to form <u>negative ions</u>.

5) The <u>number</u> of electrons lost or gained is the same as the <u>charge</u> on the ion. E.g. If 2 electrons are <u>lost</u> the charge is 2+. If 3 electrons are <u>gained</u> the charge is 3–.

## Ionic Bonding — **Transfer** of Electrons

1) When a <u>metal</u> and a <u>non-metal</u> react together, the <u>metal atom loses</u> electrons to form a <u>positively charged ion</u> and the <u>non-metal gains these electrons</u> to form a <u>negatively charged ion</u>.

2) These oppositely charged ions are <u>strongly attracted</u> to one another by <u>electrostatic forces</u>. This attraction is called an <u>ionic bond</u>.

3) The diagram below shows the formation of an <u>ionic bond</u> between sodium and chlorine to form the ionic compound <u>sodium chloride</u>.

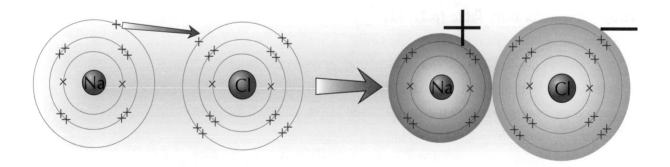

## Metals and non-metals form ionic bonds

Some atoms <u>gain</u> electrons and some atoms <u>lose</u> electrons, but they all do it to gain a <u>full outer shell</u>. An ionic bond is just the <u>attraction</u> between the electrostatic charges of the newly formed ions.

# Ions

You don't need to remember what elements form which ions — the <u>periodic table</u> is here to help you...

## Groups **1 & 2** and **6 & 7** are the Most Likely to Form **Ions**

1) The elements that <u>most readily</u> form ions are those in <u>Groups 1, 2, 6 and 7</u>.

2) <u>Group 1 and 2 elements</u> are <u>metals</u> and they <u>lose</u> electrons to form <u>positive ions</u> (<u>cations</u>).

3) <u>Group 6 and 7 elements</u> are <u>non-metals</u>. They <u>gain</u> electrons to form <u>negative ions</u> (<u>anions</u>).

4) Elements in the same <u>group</u> all have the same number of <u>outer electrons</u>. So they have to <u>lose or gain</u> the same number to get a full outer shell. And this means that they form ions with the <u>same charges</u>.

<u>Group 1</u>
elements form
<u>1+</u> ions.

<u>Group 2</u> elements
form <u>2+</u> ions.

<u>Group 6</u>
elements form
<u>2–</u> ions.

<u>Group 7</u>
elements
form <u>1–</u> ions.

*Have a look back at page 33 for how to work out electronic structures.*

A <u>sodium</u> atom (Na) is in <u>Group 1</u> so it <u>loses</u> 1 electron to form a sodium ion (Na$^+$) with the same electronic structure as <u>neon</u>: Na $\rightarrow$ Na$^+$ + e$^-$.

A <u>magnesium</u> atom (Mg) is in <u>Group 2</u> so it <u>loses</u> 2 electrons to form a magnesium ion (Mg$^{2+}$) with the same electronic structure as <u>neon</u>: Mg $\rightarrow$ Mg$^{2+}$ + 2e$^-$.

A <u>chlorine</u> atom (Cl) is in <u>Group 7</u> so it <u>gains</u> 1 electron to form a chloride ion (Cl$^-$) with the same electronic structure as <u>argon</u>: Cl + e$^-$ $\rightarrow$ Cl$^-$.

An <u>oxygen</u> atom (O) is in <u>Group 6</u> so it <u>gains</u> 2 electrons to form an oxide ion (O$^{2-}$) with the same electronic structure as <u>neon</u>: O + 2e$^-$ $\rightarrow$ O$^{2-}$.

# Ions

## Dot and Cross Diagrams Show How Ionic Bonds are Formed

Dot and cross diagrams show the arrangement of electrons in an atom or ion. Each electron is represented by a dot or a cross. So these diagrams can show which atom the electrons in an ion originally came from.

### Sodium Chloride (NaCl)

The sodium atom gives up its outer electron, becoming an Na⁺ ion. The chlorine atom picks up the electron, becoming a Cl⁻ (chloride) ion.

Here, the dots represent the Na electrons and the crosses represent the Cl electrons (all electrons are really identical, but this is a good way of following their movement).

Na
2, 8, 1
sodium atom

Cl
2, 8, 7
chlorine atom

Na⁺
2, 8
sodium ion

Cl⁻
2, 8, 8
chloride ion

NaCl (sodium chloride)

### Magnesium Oxide (MgO)

The magnesium atom gives up its two outer electrons, becoming an Mg²⁺ ion. The oxygen atom picks up the electrons, becoming an O²⁻ (oxide) ion.

Here we've only shown the outer shells of electrons on the dot and cross diagram — it makes it much simpler to see what's going on.

Mg
2, 8, 2
magnesium atom

O
2, 6
oxygen atom

Mg²⁺
2, 8
magnesium ion

O²⁻
2, 8
oxygen ion

MgO (magnesium oxide)

### Magnesium Chloride (MgCl₂)

The magnesium atom gives up its two outer electrons, becoming an Mg²⁺ ion.
The two chlorine atoms pick up one electron each, becoming two Cl⁻ (chloride) ions.

Mg
2, 8, 2
magnesium atom

Cl
2, 8, 7
chlorine atom

Cl
2, 8, 7
chlorine atom

Cl⁻
2, 8, 8
chloride ion

Mg²⁺
2, 8
magnesium ion

Cl⁻
2, 8, 8
chloride ion

MgCl₂ (magnesium chloride)

Dot and cross diagrams are useful for showing how ionic compounds are formed, but they don't show the structure of the compound, the size of the ions or how they're arranged.

## Show the electronic structure of ions with square brackets

Whether or not you're able to reproduce the drawings on this page all comes down to how well you've understood ionic bonding. (So if you're struggling, try reading the previous few pages again.)

# Ionic Compounds

An <u>ionic compound</u> is any compound that only contains <u>ionic bonds</u>...

## Ionic Compounds Have A **Regular Lattice** Structure

*The electrostatic attraction between the oppositely charged ions is ionic bonding.*

1) <u>Ionic compounds</u> have a structure called a <u>giant ionic lattice</u>.
2) The ions form a closely packed <u>regular lattice</u> arrangement and there are very strong <u>electrostatic forces of attraction</u> between <u>oppositely charged</u> ions, in <u>all directions</u> in the lattice.

A single crystal of <u>sodium chloride</u> (table salt) is <u>one giant ionic lattice</u>. The $Na^+$ and $Cl^-$ ions are held together in a regular lattice. The lattice can be represented in different ways...

*This model shows the relative sizes of the ions, as well as the regular pattern of an ionic crystal, but it only lets you see the outer layer of the compound.*

$\bullet$ = $Cl^-$  $\bullet$ = $Na^+$

*Make sure you learn what the structure of sodium chloride looks like.*

*This is a ball and stick model. It shows the regular pattern of an ionic crystal and shows how all the ions are arranged. It also suggests that the crystal extends beyond what's shown in the diagram. The model isn't to scale though, so the relative sizes of the ions may not be shown. Also, in reality, there aren't gaps between the ions.*

*The $Na^+$ and $Cl^-$ ions alternate.*

## Ionic Compounds All Have **Similar Properties**

1) They all have <u>high melting points</u> and <u>high boiling points</u> due to the <u>many strong bonds</u> between the ions. It takes lots of <u>energy</u> to overcome this attraction.
2) When they're <u>solid</u>, the ions are held in place, so the compounds <u>can't</u> conduct electricity.
3) When ionic compounds <u>melt</u>, the ions are <u>free to move</u> and they'll <u>carry electric current</u>.
4) Some ionic compounds also <u>dissolve easily</u> in water. The ions <u>separate</u> and are all <u>free to move</u> in the solution, so they'll <u>carry electric current</u>.

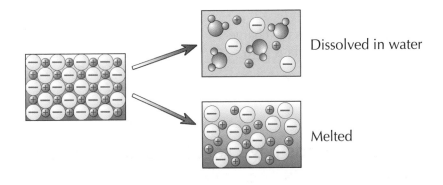

Dissolved in water

Melted

Topic 2 — Bonding, Structure and Properties of Matter

# Ionic Compounds

## Look at **Charges** to Find the **Formula** of an **Ionic Compound**

1) You might have to work out the <u>empirical formula</u> of an
ionic compound from a diagram of the compound.

2) If it's a <u>dot and cross</u> diagram, count up how <u>many</u> atoms there are of
<u>each element</u>. Write this down to give you the empirical formula.

3) If you're given a 3D diagram of the ionic lattice, <u>use</u> it to
work out <u>what ions</u> are in the ionic compound.

4) You'll then have to <u>balance</u> the charges of the ions so that the overall charge on the compound is zero.

**EXAMPLE:**

**What's the empirical formula of the ionic compound shown below?**

= Potassium ion

= Oxide ion

1) Look at the diagram to work out what ions are in the compound.

The compound contains potassium and oxide ions.

2) Work out what <u>charges</u> the ions will form.

Potassium is in Group 1 so forms 1+ ions. Oxygen is in Group 6 so forms 2− ions.

3) <u>Balance</u> the charges so the charge of the empirical formula is <u>zero</u>.

A potassium ion only has a 1+ charge, so you'll need two of them to balance out the 2− charge of an oxide ion. The empirical formula is $K_2O$.

**EXAMPLE:**

**What's the empirical formula of the ionic compound shown below?**

= Chloride ion

= Caesium ion

1) Look at the diagram to work out what ions are in the compound.

The compound contains caesium ions and chloride ions.

2) Work out what <u>charges</u> the ions will form.

Caesium is in Group 1 so forms 1+ ions. Chlorine is in Group 7 so forms 1− ions.

3) <u>Balance</u> the charges so the charge of the empirical formula is <u>zero</u>.

A caesium ion has a 1+ charge, so you only need one to balance out the 1− charge of the chloride ion. The empirical formula is CsCl.

## Ionic compounds have regular lattice structures

As long as you can find the <u>charge</u> of the ions in an ionic compound, you can work out the
<u>empirical formula</u>. Try practising with different ionic compounds.

# Warm-Up & Exam Questions

Congratulations you got to the end of the pages on ions — time to make sure you know them back to front...

## Warm-Up Questions

1) What is an ion?
2) What is the charge on a ion formed from a Group 2 element?
3) What is the charge on a ion formed from a Group 7 element?
4) Sodium chloride has a giant ionic structure. Does it have a high or a low boiling point?
5) Why do some ionic compounds conduct electricity when dissolved in water?
6) What is the formula of the compound containing $Al^{3+}$ and $OH^-$ ions only?

## Exam Questions

1    **Figure 1** shows the electronic structures of sodium and fluorine.

**Figure 1**

 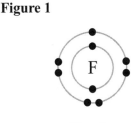

Sodium                    Fluorine

1.1   Describe what will happen when sodium and fluorine react, in terms of electrons.

*[2 marks]*

1.2   When sodium and fluorine react they form an ionic compound.
Describe the structure of an ionic compound

*[3 marks]*

2    When lithium reacts with oxygen it forms the ionic compound $Li_2O$.

2.1   Name the compound formed.

*[1 mark]*

2.2   Complete **Figure 2** below using arrows to show how the electrons are transferred when $Li_2O$ is formed.
Show the electron arrangements and the charges on the ions formed.

**Figure 2**

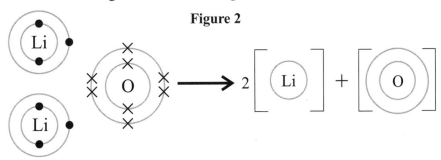

*[3 marks]*

2.3   Explain why $Li_2O$ conducts electricity when molten.

*[2 marks]*

2.4   Lithium forms an ionic compound with chlorine.
What is the formula of this compound? Explain why this is.

*[2 marks]*

# Covalent Bonding

Some elements bond ionically (see page 46) but others form strong <u>covalent</u> bonds.
This is where atoms <u>share</u> electrons with each other so that they've got full outer shells.

## Covalent Bonds — Sharing Electrons

1) When <u>non-metal</u> atoms bond together, they <u>share</u> pairs of electrons to make <u>covalent bonds</u>.

2) The positively charged nuclei of the bonded atoms are attracted to the shared pair of electrons by <u>electrostatic forces</u>, making covalent bonds very <u>strong</u>.

3) Atoms only share electrons in their <u>outer shells</u> (highest energy levels).

4) Each single <u>covalent bond</u> provides one <u>extra</u> shared electron for each atom.

5) Each atom involved generally makes <u>enough</u> covalent bonds to <u>fill up</u> its outer shell. Having a full outer shell gives them the electronic structure of a <u>noble gas</u>, which is very <u>stable</u>.

6) Covalent bonding happens in <u>compounds</u> of <u>non-metals</u> (e.g. $H_2O$) and in <u>non-metal elements</u> (e.g. $Cl_2$).

## There are Different Ways of Drawing Covalent Bonds

1) You can use <u>dot and cross diagrams</u> to show the bonding in covalent compounds.

2) Electrons drawn in the <u>overlap</u> between the outer orbitals of two atoms are <u>shared</u> between those atoms.

3) Dot and cross diagrams are useful for showing <u>which atoms</u> the electrons in a covalent bond come from, but they <u>don't</u> show the relative sizes of the atoms, or how the atoms are <u>arranged</u> in space.

*You don't have to draw the orbitals in dot and cross diagrams. The important thing is that you get all the dots and crosses in the right places.*

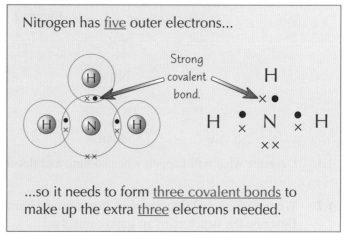

Nitrogen has <u>five</u> outer electrons...

Strong covalent bond.

...so it needs to form <u>three covalent bonds</u> to make up the extra <u>three</u> electrons needed.

Covalent bond

4) The <u>displayed formula</u> of ammonia ($NH_3$) shows the covalent bonds as single lines between atoms.

5) This is a great way of showing <u>how</u> atoms are connected in <u>large</u> molecules. However, they <u>don't</u> show the <u>3D structure</u> of the molecule, or <u>which atoms</u> the electrons in the covalent bond have come from.

6) The 3D model of ammonia shows the <u>atoms</u>, the <u>covalent bonds</u> and their <u>arrangement</u> in space next to each other. But 3D models can quickly get <u>confusing</u> for large molecules where there are lots of atoms to include. They don't show <u>where</u> the electrons in the bonds have <u>come from</u>, either.

7) You can find the <u>molecular formula</u> of a simple molecular compound from <u>any</u> of these diagrams by <u>counting up</u> how many atoms of each element there are.

*A molecular formula shows you how many atoms of each element are in a molecule.*

**EXAMPLE:** **A diagram of the molecule ethane is shown on the right. Use the diagram to find the molecular formula of ethane.**

In the diagram, there are two carbon atoms and six hydrogen atoms. So the molecular formula is $C_2H_6$.

# Covalent Bonding

## Learn Some Examples of Simple Molecular Substances

Simple molecular substances are made up of molecules containing a few atoms joined together by covalent bonds. Here are some common examples that you should know...

### Hydrogen, $H_2$

Hydrogen atoms have just one electron. They only need one more to complete the first shell...

OR  H—H  OR  H $\overset{\times}{\underset{\bullet}{}}$ H

...so they often form single covalent bonds, either with other hydrogen atoms or with other elements, to achieve this.

### Chlorine, $Cl_2$

Each chlorine atom needs just one more electron to complete the outer shell...

OR  Cl—Cl  OR

...so two chlorine atoms can share one pair of electrons and form a single covalent bond.

### Oxygen, $O_2$

Each oxygen atom needs two more electrons to complete its outer shell...

OR  O═O  OR

...so in oxygen gas two oxygen atoms share two pairs of electrons with each other making a double covalent bond.

### Nitrogen, $N_2$

A nitrogen atom needs three more electrons to complete its outer shell...

OR  N≡N  OR

...so two nitrogen atoms share three pairs of electrons to fill their outer shells. This creates a triple bond.

### Hydrogen chloride, HCl

This is very similar to $H_2$ and $Cl_2$...

OR  H—Cl  OR

...again, both atoms only need one more electron to complete their outer shells.

# Covalent Bonding

## Methane, CH₄

Carbon has <u>four outer electrons</u>, which is <u>half</u> a full shell...

It can form <u>four covalent bonds</u> with <u>hydrogen</u> atoms to fill up its outer shell.

## Water, H₂O

Make sure you can also draw the dot and cross diagram of ammonia, NH₃, which is on page 52.

In <u>water molecules</u>, the oxygen shares a pair of electrons with two H atoms to form two <u>single covalent bonds</u>.

## Properties of **Simple Molecular** Substances

1) Substances containing <u>covalent bonds</u> usually have <u>simple molecular structures</u>, like the examples shown above and on the previous page.

2) The atoms within the molecules are held together by <u>very strong covalent bonds</u>. By contrast, the forces of attraction <u>between</u> these molecules are <u>very weak</u>.

3) To melt or boil a simple molecular compound, you only need to break these <u>feeble intermolecular forces</u> and <u>not</u> the covalent bonds. So the melting and boiling points are <u>very low</u>, because the molecules are <u>easily parted</u> from each other.

4) Most molecular substances are <u>gases or liquids</u> at room temperature.

5) As molecules get <u>bigger</u>, the strength of the intermolecular forces <u>increases</u>, so <u>more energy</u> is needed to break them, and the melting and boiling points <u>increase</u>.

6) Molecular compounds <u>don't conduct electricity</u>, simply because they <u>aren't charged</u>, so there are <u>no free electrons</u> or ions.

Weak intermolecular forces

Chlorine

Oxygen

## Covalent bonding involves sharing electrons

**EXAM TIP** You might be asked to draw a <u>dot and cross diagram</u> for a simple molecule in the exam. The ones shown on this page and the previous one are good ones to learn (oh, and ammonia is handy too).

# Warm-Up & Exam Questions

The questions on this page are all about covalent bonding. Go through them and if you have any problems, make sure you look back at the relevant pages again until you've got to grips with it.

## Warm-Up Questions

1) What is a covalent bond?
2) How many covalent bonds does a molecule of nitrogen have?
3) In which states are most simple molecular substances at room temperature?
4) Which forces are stronger in simple molecular substances
   — covalent bonds or intermolecular forces?
5) What forces need to be overcome to boil a simple molecular compound?

## Exam Questions

**1** Methane is a covalently bonded molecule with the formula $CH_4$.

Complete the dot and cross diagram for the methane molecule.
Show only the outer electrons.

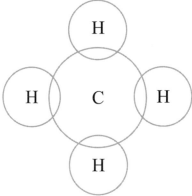

*[2 marks]*

**2** Dot and cross diagrams can be used to show the position of electrons in covalent molecules.

**2.1** Draw a dot and cross diagram for oxygen ($O_2$). Only show the outer electrons.

*[2 marks]*

**2.2** Nitrogen is in Group 5 of the periodic table.
How many bonds does it need to make to gain a full outer shell?

*[1 mark]*

**3** Hydrogen chloride is a simple molecular substance.

**3.1** Explain why hydrogen chloride has poor electrical conductivity.

*[1 mark]*

**3.2** Explain how the atoms are held together in a molecule of hydrogen chloride.

*[2 marks]*

**3.3** A molecule of hydrogen chloride has a stronger bond than a molecule of chlorine ($Cl_2$).
However, hydrogen chloride boils at −85 °C, whereas chlorine boils at −34 °C.
Suggest and explain why chlorine has a higher boiling point than hydrogen chloride.

*[3 marks]*

# Polymers

Most polymers are held together with <u>covalent bonds</u>.  However, these molecules are
a bit different to the simple covalent compounds you have already met...

## Polymers Are **Long Chains** of **Repeating** Units

1) In a polymer, lots of <u>small units</u> are linked together to form a <u>long molecule</u> that has
   repeating sections.  All the atoms in a polymer are joined by strong <u>covalent bonds</u>.

Instead of drawing out a whole long polymer molecule (which can contain thousands or even
millions of atoms), you can draw the <u>shortest</u> repeating section, called the <u>repeating unit</u>, like this:

This polymer
is called
'poly(ethene)'.

The bonds through the
brackets join up to the
next repeating unit.

'*n*' is a large number.
It tells you that the unit's
repeated lots of times.

The bit in
brackets is the
repeating unit.

To find the <u>molecular formula</u> of a polymer, write down the molecular
formula of the <u>repeating unit</u> in <u>brackets</u>, and put an '<u>n</u>' outside.
So for <u>poly(ethene)</u>, the molecular formula of the polymer is $(C_2H_4)_n$.

2) The intermolecular forces between polymer molecules are <u>larger</u> than
   between simple covalent molecules, so <u>more energy</u> is needed to break them.
   This means most polymers are <u>solid</u> at room temperature.

3) The intermolecular forces are still <u>weaker</u> than ionic or covalent bonds, so they
   generally have <u>lower</u> boiling points than <u>ionic</u> or <u>giant molecular</u> compounds.

## Polymers are very large molecules

Make sure you can work out the <u>molecular formula</u> of a polymer.  To do this you need to be comfortable
with what the <u>repeating unit</u> of a polymer is.  There's more about polymers on page 118.

# Giant Covalent Structures

Polymers and simple molecular substances aren't the only compounds held together by covalent bonds. Giant covalent structures are too — some are found in nature, while others can be made in a lab.

## Giant Covalent Structures Are Macromolecules

1) In giant covalent structures, all the atoms are bonded to each other by strong covalent bonds.

2) They have very high melting and boiling points as lots of energy is needed to break the covalent bonds between the atoms.

3) They don't contain charged particles, so they don't conduct electricity — not even when molten (except for a few weird exceptions such as graphite, see next page).

4) The main examples are diamond and graphite, which are both made from carbon atoms only, and silicon dioxide (silica).

### Diamond

Each carbon atom forms four covalent bonds in a very rigid giant covalent structure.

*There's more about diamond and graphite, as well as other types of carbon structure on the next page.*

### Graphite

Each carbon atom forms three covalent bonds to create layers of hexagons. Each carbon atom also has one delocalised (free) electron.

### Silicon dioxide

silicon

oxygen

Sometimes called silica, this is what sand is made of. Each grain of sand is one giant structure of silicon and oxygen.

## Giant covalent structures have high melting and boiling points

To melt or boil a giant covalent structure, you have to break very strong covalent bonds. The high melting and boiling points of diamond, graphite and silicon are caused by the strength of their covalent bonds.

# Allotropes of Carbon

Allotropes are just different structural forms of the same element in the same physical state, e.g. they're all solids. Carbon has quite a few allotropes with lots of different properties.

## Diamond is Very Hard

1) Diamond has a giant covalent structure, made up of carbon atoms that each form four covalent bonds. This makes diamond really hard.

2) Those strong covalent bonds take a lot of energy to break and give diamond a very high melting point.

3) It doesn't conduct electricity because it has no free electrons or ions.

## Graphite Contains Sheets of Hexagons

1) In graphite, each carbon atom only forms three covalent bonds, creating sheets of carbon atoms arranged in hexagons.

2) There aren't any covalent bonds between the layers — they're only held together weakly, so they're free to move over each other. This makes graphite soft and slippery, so it's ideal as a lubricating material.

3) Graphite's got a high melting point — the covalent bonds in the layers need loads of energy to break.

4) Only three out of each carbon's four outer electrons are used in bonds, so each carbon atom has one electron that's delocalised (free) and can move. So graphite conducts electricity and thermal energy.

## Graphene is One Layer of Graphite

1) Graphene is a sheet of carbon atoms joined together in hexagons.

2) The sheet is just one atom thick, making it a two-dimensional compound.

3) The network of covalent bonds makes it very strong. It's also incredibly light, so can be added to composite materials to improve their strength without adding much weight.

4) Like graphite, it contains delocalised electrons so can conduct electricity through the whole structure. This means it has the potential to be used in electronics.

---

## Diamond, graphite and graphene contain exactly the same atoms

The different substances on this page are made purely from carbon — there's no difference at all in their atoms. The difference in properties is all down to the way the atoms are held together.

---

# Allotropes of Carbon

Diamond, graphite, and graphene aren't the only allotropes of carbon.
In fact, we are discovering and making new allotropes of carbon all the time.

## Fullerenes Form Spheres and Tubes

1) Fullerenes are molecules of carbon, shaped like closed tubes or hollow balls.

2) They're mainly made up of carbon atoms arranged in hexagons, but can also contain pentagons (rings of five carbon atoms) or heptagons (rings of seven carbon atoms).

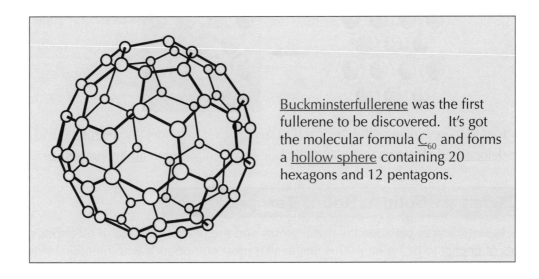

Buckminsterfullerene was the first fullerene to be discovered. It's got the molecular formula $C_{60}$ and forms a hollow sphere containing 20 hexagons and 12 pentagons.

3) Fullerenes can be used to 'cage' other molecules. The fullerene structure forms around another atom or molecule, which is then trapped inside. This could be used to deliver a drug into the body.

4) Fullerenes have a huge surface area, so they could help make great industrial catalysts — individual catalyst molecules could be attached to the fullerenes (the bigger the surface area the better).

*Catalysts speed up the rates of chemical reactions without being used up themselves (see p.102).*

5) Fullerenes also make great lubricants.

1) Fullerenes can form nanotubes — tiny carbon cylinders.
2) The ratio between the length and the diameter of nanotubes is very high.
3) Nanotubes can conduct both electricity and thermal energy (heat).
4) They also have a high tensile strength (they don't break when they're stretched).
5) Technology that uses very small particles such as nanotubes is called nanotechnology. Nanotubes can be used in electronics or to strengthen materials without adding much weight, such as in tennis racket frames.

## Fullerenes are really useful materials

Before you move on, make sure you can explain the properties of the allotropes of carbon. While you are at it, don't forget to learn the potential uses of fullerenes that are mentioned on this page.

# Metallic Bonding

Ever wondered what gives a metal its properties?  Most of it comes down to bonding...

## Metallic Bonding Involves Delocalised Electrons

1)  <u>Metals</u> also consist of a <u>giant structure</u>.

2)  The electrons in the <u>outer shell</u> of the metal atoms are <u>delocalised</u> (free to move around).  There are strong forces of <u>electrostatic attraction</u> between the <u>positive metal ions</u> and the shared <u>negative electrons</u>.

3)  These forces of attraction <u>hold</u> the <u>atoms</u> together in a <u>regular</u> structure and are known as <u>metallic bonding</u>.  Metallic bonding is very <u>strong</u>.

Metal atom

Delocalised electrons

4)  Substances that are held together by metallic bonding include metallic <u>elements</u> and <u>alloys</u> (see below).

5)  It's the <u>delocalised electrons</u> in the metallic bonds which produce <u>all</u> the properties of metals...

## Most Metals are Solid at Room Temperature

The electrostatic forces between the metal atoms and the delocalised sea of electrons are very <u>strong</u>, so need <u>lots of energy</u> to be broken.  This means that most compounds with metallic bonds have very <u>high</u> melting and boiling points, so they're generally <u>solid</u> at room temperature.

## Metals are Good Conductors of Electricity and Heat

The <u>delocalised electrons</u> carry electrical current and thermal (heat) energy through the whole structure, so metals are good <u>conductors</u> of <u>electricity</u> and <u>heat</u>.

## Most Metals are Malleable

The layers of atoms in a metal can <u>slide</u> over each other, making metals <u>malleable</u> — this means that they can be <u>bent</u> or <u>hammered</u> or <u>rolled</u> into <u>flat sheets</u>.

## Alloys are Harder Than Pure Metals

1)  <u>Pure metals</u> often aren't quite right for certain jobs — they're often <u>too soft</u> when they're pure so are mixed with other elements to make them <u>harder</u>.  Most of the metals we use everyday are <u>alloys</u> — a <u>mixture</u> of <u>two or more metals</u> or a <u>metal and another element</u>.  Alloys are <u>harder</u> and so more useful than pure metals.

2)  Different elements have <u>different sized atoms</u>.  So when another element is mixed with a pure metal, the new metal atoms will <u>distort</u> the layers of metal atoms, making it more difficult for them to slide over each other.  This makes alloys <u>harder</u> than pure metals.

## Metallic bonding is what makes metals, well... metals

You should understand what <u>metallic bonding</u> is, and be able to relate how it causes metals to have the <u>properties</u> they do.  Also, don't forget to learn the differences between <u>alloys</u> and <u>pure metals</u>.

# Warm-Up & Exam Questions

Lots of information to learn on the previous few pages — here are some questions to test yourself on.

## Warm-Up Questions

1) How are the repeating units in a polymer bonded together?
2) At room temperature, what state are most polymers in?
3) Describe the differences in the hardness and electrical conductivity of diamond and graphite.
4) Which fullerene was the first to be discovered?
5) Explain why most metals are malleable.

## Exam Questions

**1** Silicon carbide has a giant covalent structure and is a solid at room temperature.

**1.1** Explain, in terms of its bonding and structure, why silicon carbide has a high melting point.

*[2 marks]*

**1.2** Give **one** other example of a substance with a giant covalent structure.

*[1 mark]*

**2** Graphite, diamond and fullerenes are entirely made from carbon but have different properties.

**2.1** Why does the structure of graphite make it a useful lubricant?

*[2 marks]*

**2.2** Using your knowledge of the structure of diamond, suggest why it is useful as a cutting tool.

*[2 marks]*

**2.3** Suggest **one** possible use for fullerenes.

*[1 mark]*

**2.4** Explain why graphite is able to conduct electricity.

*[1 mark]*

**3** **Figure 1** shows the arrangement of atoms in pure iron.

**Figure 1**

**3.1** Steel is an alloy of iron and carbon.
Sketch a similar diagram to show the arrangement of atoms in steel.

*[2 marks]*

**3.2** Steel is harder than iron. Explain why.

*[3 marks]*

# States of Matter

You can explain quite a bit of stuff in chemistry if you can get your head round this lot.

## The Three States of Matter — Solid, Liquid and Gas

Materials come in three different forms — solid, liquid and gas. These are the three states of matter. Which state something is at a certain temperature (solid, liquid or gas) depends on how strong the forces of attraction are between the particles of the material. How strong the forces are depends on THREE THINGS:

1) the material (the structure of the substance and the type of bonds holding the particles together),

2) the temperature,

3) the pressure.

*The particles could be atoms, ions or molecules.*

You can use a model called particle theory to explain how the particles in a material behave in each of the three states of matter by considering each particle as a small, solid, inelastic sphere.

### Solids

1) In solids, there are strong forces of attraction between particles, which holds them close together in fixed positions to form a very regular lattice arrangement.

2) The particles don't move from their positions, so all solids keep a definite shape and volume, and don't flow like liquids.

3) The particles vibrate about their positions — the hotter the solid becomes, the more they vibrate (causing solids to expand slightly when heated).

### Liquids

1) In liquids, there's a weak force of attraction between the particles. They're randomly arranged and free to move past each other, but they tend to stick closely together.

2) Liquids have a definite volume but don't keep a definite shape, and will flow to fill the bottom of a container.

3) The particles are constantly moving with random motion. The hotter the liquid gets, the faster they move. This causes liquids to expand slightly when heated.

### Gases

1) In gases, the force of attraction between the particles is very weak — they're free to move and are far apart. The particles in gases travel in straight lines.

2) Gases don't keep a definite shape or volume and will always fill any container.

3) The particles move constantly with random motion. The hotter the gas gets, the faster they move. Gases either expand when heated, or their pressure increases.

Particle theory is a great model for explaining the three states of matter, but it isn't perfect. In reality, the particles aren't solid or inelastic and they aren't spheres — they're atoms, ions or molecules. Also, the model doesn't show the forces between the particles, so there's no way of knowing how strong they are.

# States of Matter

## Substances Can **Change** from **One State to Another**

Physical changes don't change the particles — just their arrangement or their energy.

1) When a solid is heated, its particles gain more energy.

2) This makes the particles vibrate more, which weakens the forces that hold the solid together.

3) At a certain temperature, called the melting point the particles have enough energy to break free from their positions. This is called MELTING and the solid turns into a liquid.

4) When a liquid is heated, again the particles get even more energy.

5) This energy makes the particles move faster, which weakens and breaks the bonds holding the liquid together.

6) At a certain temperature, called the boiling point, the particles have enough energy to break their bonds. This is BOILING (or evaporating). The liquid becomes a gas.

Solid

Liquid

melting       freezing

boiling       condensing

Gas

12) At the melting point, so many bonds have formed between the particles that they're held in place. The liquid becomes a solid. This is FREEZING.

11) There's not enough energy to overcome the attraction between the particles, so more bonds form between them.

10) When a liquid cools, the particles have less energy, so move around less.

9) At the boiling point, so many bonds have formed between the gas particles that the gas becomes a liquid. This is called CONDENSING.

8) Bonds form between the particles.

7) As a gas cools, the particles no longer have enough energy to overcome the forces of attraction between them.

So, the amount of energy needed for a substance to change state depends on how strong the forces between particles are. The stronger the forces, the more energy is needed to break them, and so the higher the melting and boiling points of the substance.

Topic 2 — Bonding, Structure and Properties of Matter

# States of Matter

The state a substance is in can be really important in working out <u>how it will react</u>. This page is all about how chemists show what the <u>state</u> of a substance is and how they <u>predict</u> what state a substance will be in.

## State Symbols Tell You the State of a Substance in an Equation

You saw on page 20 how a chemical reaction can be shown using a <u>word equation</u> or <u>symbol equation</u>. Symbol equations can also include <u>state symbols</u> next to each substance — they tell you what <u>physical state</u> the reactants and products are in:

$$\text{(s) — solid \quad (l) — liquid \quad (g) — gas \quad (aq) — aqueous}$$

'Aqueous' means 'dissolved in water'.

Here are a <u>couple</u> of examples:

> <u>Aqueous</u> hydrogen chloride reacts with <u>solid</u> calcium carbonate to form <u>aqueous</u> calcium chloride, <u>liquid</u> water and carbon dioxide <u>gas</u>:
> $$2HCl_{(aq)} + CaCO_{3(s)} \rightarrow CaCl_{2(aq)} + H_2O_{(l)} + CO_{2(g)}$$

> Chlorine gas reacts with <u>aqueous</u> potassium iodide to form <u>aqueous</u> potassium chloride and <u>solid</u> iodine:
> $$Cl_{2(g)} + 2KI_{(aq)} \rightarrow 2KCl_{(aq)} + I_{2(s)}$$

## You Might Need to Predict the State of a Substance

1) You might be asked to predict <u>what state</u> a substance is in at a <u>certain temperature</u>.

2) If the temperature's <u>below</u> the <u>melting point</u> of substance, it'll be a <u>solid</u>. If it's <u>above</u> the <u>boiling point</u>, it'll be a <u>gas</u>. If it's <u>in between</u> the two points, then it's a <u>liquid</u>.

**EXAMPLE:**

**Which of the molecular substances in the table is a liquid at room temperature (25 °C)?**

| | Melting point | Boiling point |
|---|---|---|
| **oxygen** | −219 °C | −183 °C |
| **nitrogen** | −210 °C | −196 °C |
| **bromine** | −7 °C | 59 °C |

Oxygen and nitrogen have boiling points below 25 °C, so will both be gases at room temperature.

So the answer's bromine. It melts at −7 °C and boils at 59 °C. So, it'll be a liquid at room temperature.

*The bulk properties such as the melting point of a material depend on how lots of atoms interact together. An atom on its own doesn't have these properties.*

## Physical changes are reversible

**REVISION TIP** Make sure you can describe what happens to particles, and the forces between them, as a substance is <u>heated</u> and <u>cooled</u>. Don't forget to learn the technical terms for each <u>state change</u>.

# Warm-Up & Exam Questions

Reckon you know all there is to know about this section?  Have a go at these questions and see how you get on.  If you get stuck on something — just flick back and give it another read through.

## Warm-Up Questions

1) What three factors are the strength of the forces between particles dependent on?
2) What state of matter has a fixed lattice arrangement?
3) Is the strength of the attraction between particles of a gas strong or weak?
4) What happens to the particles in a gas when it is heated?
5) Describe what happens when a gas condenses.
6) Write down how you would show that sodium ions ($Na^+$) are in solution in a symbol equation.

## Exam Questions

1.1 **Figure 1** shows a vessel in a distillery.  The walls of the vessel are solid copper.

**Figure 1**

Complete the sentences about solids using words from the box.
Each word may be used once, more than once or not at all.

| | | | | |
|---|---|---|---|---|
| weak | move | colder | hotter | random |
| strong | expand | heavier | dissolve | regular |

In solids, there are ........................... forces of attraction between particles,

which hold them in fixed positions in a ........................... arrangement.

The particles don't ........................... from their positions, so solids keep their shape.

The ........................... the solid becomes, the more the particles in the solid vibrate.

*[4 marks]*

1.2 Inside the vessel, liquid ethanol is turned into ethanol gas.
Describe the changes in arrangement, movement and energy of the
particles when the liquid ethanol is heated to become a gas.

*[2 marks]*

2 This question is on states of matter. (Grade 6-7)

2.1 Using particle theory, explain why gases fill their containers.

*[2 marks]*

2.2 Using particle theory, explain why liquids flow.

*[2 marks]*

2.3 Chlorine has a melting point of –101.5 °C and a boiling point of –34 °C.
Predict what state chlorine will be in at –29 °C.

*[1 mark]*

# Revision Summary for Topic 2

That wraps up <u>Topic 2</u> — time to put yourself to the test and find out <u>how much you really know</u>.
- Try these questions and <u>tick off each one</u> when you <u>get it right</u>.
- When you've done <u>all the questions</u> under a heading and are <u>completely happy</u> with it, tick it off.

## Ions and Ionic Compounds (p.46-50) ☑

1) Describe how an ionic bond forms.

2) Which group of the periodic table contains elements which form ions with the following charges?
   a) +1
   b) –1

3) Sketch dot and cross diagrams to show the formation of:
   a) sodium chloride   b) magnesium oxide   c) magnesium chloride

4) Describe the structure of a crystal of sodium chloride.

5) List the main properties of ionic compounds.

## Covalent Bonding (p.52-54) ☑

6) Describe how covalent bonds form.

7) Sketch dot and cross diagrams showing the bonding in a molecule of:
   a) hydrogen    b) water    c) ammonia

8) Explain why simple molecular compounds typically have low melting and boiling points.

## Covalent Structures and Metallic Bonding (p.56-60) ☑

9) Describe the structure of a polymer.

10) What type of bond occurs between carbon atoms in diamond?

11) Describe the structure of graphene.

12) Explain how fullerenes could be used to deliver drugs into the body.

13) What is metallic bonding?

14) Explain why metals have the following properties:
   a) good conduction of heat and electricity
   b) solid at room temperature

## States of Matter (p.62-64) ☑

15) Name the three states of matter.

16) What is the name of the temperature at which a liquid becomes a gas?

17) Name the process that occurs when a liquid becomes a solid.

18) How does the strength of the forces between particles influence the temperature
   at which a substance changes state?

19) What is the state symbol of a solid substance?

## Relative Formula Mass

Calculating <u>relative formula mass</u> is straight forward enough, but things can get a bit more confusing when you start working out the <u>percentage compositions</u> of compounds.

*You can find the relative atomic mass ($A_r$) of an element from the periodic table — it's the same as its mass number. See page 18 for more.*

## Compounds Have a **Relative Formula Mass**, $M_r$

If you have a compound like $MgCl_2$ then it has a <u>relative formula mass</u>, <u>$M_r$</u>, which is just the relative atomic masses of all the atoms in the molecular formula <u>added together</u>.

**EXAMPLE:**   **Find the relative formula mass of $MgCl_2$.**

1) Look up the <u>relative atomic masses</u> of all the elements in the compound on the periodic table. (In the exams, you might be given the $A_r$ you need in the question.)
   $A_r$ of Mg = 24 and the $A_r$ of Cl = 35.5.

2) <u>Add up</u> all the relative atomic masses of the atoms in the compound.
   $Mg + (2 \times Cl) = 24 + (2 \times 35.5) = 95$   So $M_r$ of $MgCl_2$ = 95

   *There are two chlorine atoms in $MgCl_2$, so the relative atomic mass of chlorine needs to be multiplied by 2.*

## You Can Calculate the **% Mass** of an **Element** in a **Compound**

This is actually <u>dead easy</u> — so long as you've learnt this <u>formula</u>:

$$\text{Percentage mass of an element in a compound} = \frac{A_r \times \text{number of atoms of that element}}{M_r \text{ of the compound}} \times 100$$

**EXAMPLE:**

**Find the percentage mass of sodium in sodium carbonate, $Na_2CO_3$.**

$A_r$ of sodium = 23,   $A_r$ of carbon = 12,   $A_r$ of oxygen = 16

$M_r$ of $Na_2CO_3$ = $(2 \times 23) + 12 + (3 \times 16) = 106$

Percentage mass of sodium = $\dfrac{A_r \times \text{number of atoms of that element}}{M_r \text{ of the compound}} \times 100 = \dfrac{23 \times 2}{106} \times 100 = 43\%$

You might also come across more complicated questions where you need to work out the <u>percentage mass</u>.

**EXAMPLE:**

**A mixture contains 20% iron ions by mass. What mass of iron chloride ($FeCl_2$) would you need to provide the iron ions in 50 g of the mixture?  $A_r$ of Fe = 56, $A_r$ of Cl = 35.5.**

1) Find the <u>mass</u> of iron in the mixture.
   The mixture contains 20% iron by mass, so in 50 g there will be $50 \times \dfrac{20}{100} = 10$ g of iron.

2) Calculate the <u>percentage mass</u> of iron in <u>iron chloride</u>.
   Percentage mass of iron $= \dfrac{A_r \times \text{number of atoms of iron}}{M_r \text{ of iron chloride}} \times 100 = \dfrac{56}{56 + (2 \times 35.5)} \times 100 = 44.09...\%$

3) Calculate the <u>mass</u> of <u>iron chloride</u> that contains 10 g of iron.
   Iron chloride contains 44.09% iron by mass, so there will be 10 g of iron in $10 \div \dfrac{44.09...}{100} = 23$ g
   So you need **23 g** of iron chloride to provide the iron in 50 g of the mixture.

---

### Relative formula mass — add up all the relative atomic masses

You'll get a <u>periodic table</u> in the exams, which could be handy for these sorts of calculations — the <u>relative atomic mass</u> of an element is the <u>bigger number</u> next to the element's symbol.

# The Mole and Mass

The mole can be pretty confusing. I think it's the word that puts people off. It's difficult to see the relevance of the word "mole" to anything but a small burrowing animal.

## "The Mole" is Simply the Name Given to an Amount of a Substance

1) Just like "a million" is this many: 1 000 000; or "a billion" is this many: 1 000 000 000, so "the Avogadro constant" is this many: 602 000 000 000 000 000 000 000 or $6.02 \times 10^{23}$. And that's all it is. Just a number.

2) One mole of any substance is just an amount of that substance that contains an Avogadro number of particles — so $6.02 \times 10^{23}$ particles. The particles could be atoms, molecules, ions or electrons.

The symbol for the unit 'moles' is 'mol'.

3) So why is such a long number like the Avogadro constant used? The answer is that the mass of that number of atoms or molecules of any substance is exactly the same number of grams as the relative atomic mass ($A_r$) or relative formula mass ($M_r$) of the element or compound.

4) In other words, one mole of atoms or molecules of any substance will have a mass in grams equal to the relative formula mass ($A_r$ or $M_r$) for that substance. Here are some examples:

Carbon has an $A_r$ of 12.
So one mole of carbon weighs exactly 12 g.

Nitrogen gas, $N_2$, has an $M_r$ of 28 ($2 \times 14$).
So one mole of $N_2$ weighs exactly 28 g.

Carbon dioxide, $CO_2$, has an $M_r$ of 44 ($12 + [2 \times 16]$).
So one mole of $CO_2$ weighs exactly 44 g.

5) This means that 12 g of carbon, or 28 g of nitrogen, or 44 g of carbon dioxide, all contain the same number of particles, namely one mole or $6.02 \times 10^{23}$ atoms or molecules.

# The Mole and Mass

So you now you know what a mole is, you probably want to know how to work out the <u>number of moles</u> in a given <u>mass</u> of a substance, right?   Well you're in luck...

## Nice Formula to Find the Number of Moles in a Given Mass:

$$\text{Number of moles} = \frac{\text{mass in g (of an element or compound)}}{M_r \text{ (of the element or compound)}}$$

**EXAMPLE:** **How many moles are there in 66 g of carbon dioxide ($CO_2$)?**

1) Calculate the <u>$M_r$</u> of carbon dioxide.     $M_r$ of $CO_2$ = 12 + (16 × 2) = 44

2) Use the formula above to find     No. of moles = Mass (g) ÷ $M_r$ = 66 ÷ 44 = 1.5 mol
out how many moles there are.

You can <u>rearrange</u> the equation above using this handy <u>formula triangle</u>.
You could use it to find the <u>mass</u> of a known number of moles of a substance, or
to find the $M_r$ of a substance from a known mass and number of moles.  Just <u>cover</u>
<u>up</u> the thing you want to find with your finger and write down what's left showing.

**EXAMPLE:** **What mass of carbon is there in 4 moles of carbon dioxide?**

There are 4 moles of carbon in 4 moles of $CO_2$.

Cover up 'mass' in the formula triangle.  That leaves you with 'no. of moles × $M_r$'.

So the mass of 4 moles of carbon = 4 × 12 = 48 g

## In a Chemical Reaction, Mass is Always Conserved

1) During a chemical reaction <u>no atoms are destroyed</u> and <u>no atoms are created</u>.

2) This means there are the <u>same number and types of atoms</u> on each side of a reaction equation.

3) Because of this, no mass is lost or gained — we say that mass is <u>conserved</u> during a reaction.
For example:

$$2Li + F_2 \rightarrow 2LiF$$

In this reaction, there are <u>2 lithium atoms</u> and <u>2 fluorine atoms</u> on <u>each side</u> of the equation.

4) By <u>adding up</u> the relative formula masses of the substances on each side of a <u>balanced symbol equation</u>,
you can see that mass is conserved.  The total $M_r$ of all the reactants <u>equals</u> the total $M_r$ of the products.

**EXAMPLE:**

**Show that mass is conserved in this reaction:  $2Li + F_2 \rightarrow 2LiF$.**

1) Add up the relative formula masses on the <u>left-hand side</u> of the equation.
2 × $M_r$(Li) + 2 × $M_r$(F) = (2 × 7) + (2 × 19) = 14 + 38 = 52

2) Add up the relative formula masses on the <u>right-hand side</u> of the equation.
2 × $M_r$(LiF) = 2 × (7 + 19) = 2 × 26 = 52

The total $M_r$ on the left hand side of the equation is equal
to the total $M_r$ on the right hand side, so mass is conserved.

There's more about
balanced symbol equations
on p.21.

# The Mole and Mass

## If the Mass **Seems to Change**, There's Usually a **Gas** Involved

In some experiments, you might observe a change of mass of an unsealed reaction vessel during a reaction. There are usually two explanations for this:

### Explanation 1:

1) If the mass increases, it's probably because one of the reactants is a gas that's found in air (e.g. oxygen) and all the products are solids, liquids or aqueous.

2) Before the reaction, the gas is floating around in the air. It's there, but it's not contained in the reaction vessel, so you can't account for its mass.

3) When the gas reacts to form part of the product, it becomes contained inside the reaction vessel — so the total mass of the stuff inside the reaction vessel increases.

> For example, when a metal reacts with oxygen in an unsealed container, the mass of the container increases. The mass of the metal oxide produced equals the total mass of the metal and the oxygen that reacted from the air.
>
> $$\text{metal}_{(s)} + \text{oxygen}_{(g)} \rightarrow \text{metal oxide}_{(s)}$$

### Explanation 2:

1) If the mass decreases, it's probably because one or more of the products are gases and all the reactants are solids, liquids or aqueous.

2) Before the reaction, all the reactants are contained in the reaction vessel.

3) If the vessel isn't enclosed, then any gases can escape from the reaction vessel as they're formed. They're no longer contained in the reaction vessel, so you can't account for their mass — the total mass of the stuff inside the reaction vessel decreases.

> For example, when a metal carbonate thermally decomposes to form a metal oxide and carbon dioxide gas, the mass of the reaction vessel will decrease if it isn't sealed. But in reality, the mass of the metal oxide and the carbon dioxide produced will equal the mass of the metal carbonate that decomposed.
>
> $$\text{metal carbonate}_{(s)} \rightarrow \text{metal oxide}_{(s)} + \text{carbon dioxide}_{(g)}$$

Remember from the particle model on page 62 that a gas will expand to fill any container it's in. So if the reaction vessel isn't sealed, any gas formed expands out from the vessel, and escapes into the air around.

## Mass is ALWAYS conserved

There is quite a bit to take in on these pages, but it's all really important in everything you do in chemistry. Make sure you learn the equation on the previous page — it'll crop up again in the rest of the Topic.

# Warm-Up & Exam Questions

If you feel like you need some practice with relative masses and mole calculations, then you're in luck. Here's a nice bunch of questions for you to have a go at.

## Exam Questions

**1** Boron can form a number of covalent compounds.
Use the $A_r$ values B = 11, O = 16, F = 19 and H = 1 to calculate the relative formula masses of these boron compounds:

**1.1** BF$_3$

*[1 mark]*

**1.2** B(OH)$_3$

*[1 mark]*

**2** A student was asked to calculate the number of moles and the masses of different compounds she would be using in her lab practical.
State the formula used to work out the number of moles from the mass of a compound.

*[1 mark]*

**3** A teacher has a 140 g sample of potassium hydroxide (KOH).
Calculate, in grams, how much more KOH the teacher needs to have a 4 mole sample.

*[3 marks]*

**4** A scientist burnt 300 g of metal **X** in an unsealed beaker. She then weighed the contents of the beaker and found that it now weighed 500 g.
All of the metal **X** reacted to form a single product, a metal oxide.

**4.1** Explain why the mass increased during the reaction.

*[1 mark]*

**4.2** Analysis of the metal oxide shows that it contains 40% oxygen by mass.
What is the percentage mass of metal **X** in the oxide?

*[1 mark]*

**4.3** The scientist plans to use the metal oxide as part of a mixture.
The final mixture contains 24% metal **X** by mass, which all comes from the metal oxide.
What mass of the metal oxide was used to make 8.0 g of the mixture?

*[2 marks]*

# The Mole and Equations

Remember the 'number of moles = mass ÷ $M_r$' equation from page 69? This is where it comes into its own.

## The **Numbers** in **Chemical Equations** Mean Different Things

Remember those balanced equations back on page 21? Well, the big numbers in front of the chemical formulas of the reactants and products tell you how many moles of each substance takes part or is formed during the reaction. For example:

$$Mg_{(s)} + 2HCl_{(aq)} \rightarrow MgCl_{2(aq)} + H_{2(g)}$$

In this reaction, 1 mole of magnesium and 2 moles of hydrochloric acid react together to form 1 mole of magnesium chloride and 1 mole of hydrogen gas.

*The little numbers tell you how many atoms of each element there are in each of the substances.*

## You Can **Balance Equations** Using **Reacting Masses**

If you know the masses of the reactants and products that took part in a reaction, you can work out the balanced symbol equation for the reaction. Here are the steps you should take:

1) Divide the mass of each substance by its relative formula mass to find the number of moles.
2) Divide the number of moles of each substance by the smallest number of moles in the reaction.
3) If any of the numbers aren't whole numbers, multiply all the numbers by the same amount so that they all become whole numbers.
4) Write the balanced symbol equation for the reaction by putting these numbers in front of the chemical formulas.

**EXAMPLE:** 8.1 g of zinc oxide (ZnO) reacts completely with 0.60 g of carbon to form 2.2 g of carbon dioxide and 6.5 g of zinc. Write a balanced symbol equation for this reaction. $A_r(C) = 12$, $A_r(O) = 16$, $A_r(Zn) = 65$.

1) Work out $M_r$ for each of the substances in the reaction:
   ZnO: 65 + 16 = 81          C: 12          $CO_2$: 12 + (2 × 16) = 44          Zn: 65

2) Divide the mass of each substance by its $M_r$ to calculate how many moles of each substance reacted or were produced:

   ZnO: $\frac{8.1}{81}$ = 0.10 mol          C: $\frac{0.60}{12}$ = 0.050 mol

   $CO_2$: $\frac{2.2}{44}$ = 0.050 mol          Zn: $\frac{6.5}{65}$ = 0.10

3) Divide by the smallest number of moles, which is 0.050:

   ZnO: $\frac{0.10}{0.050}$ = 2.0          C: $\frac{0.050}{0.050}$ = 1.0

   $CO_2$: $\frac{0.050}{0.050}$ = 1.0          Zn: $\frac{0.10}{0.050}$ = 2.0

   *These numbers give the ratio of the amounts of each substance in the reaction equation.*

4) The numbers are all whole numbers, so you can write out the balanced symbol equation straight away:

$$2ZnO + C \rightarrow CO_2 + 2Zn$$

 ## Practise, Practise, Practise

You can check your final answer to questions like the one in the example above by making sure there's the same number of atoms of each element on both sides of the equation.

# The Mole and Equations

Reactions don't go on forever — you need stuff in the reaction flask that can react.  If one reactant gets completely used up in a reaction before the rest, then the reaction will stop.  That reactant's called limiting.

## Reactions **Stop** When **One** Reactant is **Used Up**

When some magnesium carbonate ($MgCO_3$) is placed into a beaker of hydrochloric acid,
you can tell a reaction is taking place because you see lots of bubbles of gas being given off.
After a while, the amount of fizzing slows down and the reaction eventually stops...

1) The reaction stops when all of one of the reactants is used up.
   Any other reactants are in excess.
   They're usually added in excess to make sure that the other reactant is used up.

2) The reactant that's used up in a reaction is called the limiting
   reactant (because it limits the amount of product that's formed).

3) The amount of product formed is directly proportional to the amount of limiting reactant.
   For example, if you halve the amount of limiting reactant, the amount of product formed
   will also underline halve.  If you underline double the amount of limiting reactant, the amount of product will
   underline double (as long as it is still the limiting reactant).

4) This is because if you add underline more reactant there
   will be more reactant particles to take part in the
   reaction, which means more product particles.

## The Amount of **Product** Depends on the **Limiting Reactant**

You can calculate the mass of a product formed in a reaction by using the
mass of the limiting reactant and the balanced reaction equation.

1) Write out the balanced equation.

2) Work out relative formula masses ($M_r$) of the reactant and product you want.

3) Find out how many moles there are of the substance you know the mass of.

4) Use the balanced equation to work out how many moles there'll be of the other
   substance.  In this case, that's how many moles of product will be made of this many
   moles of reactant.

5) Use the number of moles to calculate the mass.

# The Mole and Concentration Equations

## Here's an **Example** Mass Calculation:

**EXAMPLE:** Calculate the mass of aluminium oxide formed when 135 g of aluminium is burned in air.

1) Write out the balanced equation: $4Al + 3O_2 \rightarrow 2Al_2O_3$

   You don't have to find $M_r$ of oxygen because it's in excess.

2) Calculate the relative formula masses: Al: 27   $Al_2O_3$: $(2 \times 27) + (3 \times 16) = 102$

3) Calculate the number of moles of aluminium in 135 g: Moles $= \dfrac{\text{mass}}{M_r} = \dfrac{135}{27} = 5$

4) Look at the ratio of moles in the equation:  4 moles of Al react to produce 2 moles of $Al_2O_3$ — half the number of moles are produced. So 5 moles of Al will react to produce 2.5 moles of $Al_2O_3$

   *If the question asked for the number of moles of aluminium oxide formed, you'd stop here.*

5) Calculate the mass of 2.5 moles of aluminium oxide:  mass = moles $\times M_r = 2.5 \times 102 = 255$ g

The mass of product (in this case aluminium oxide) is called the yield of a reaction. Masses you calculate in this way are called theoretical yields. In practice you never get 100% of the yield, so the amount of product you get will be less than you calculated.

## **Concentration** is a Measure of How **Crowded** Things Are

1) Lots of reactions in chemistry take place between substances that are dissolved in a solution. The amount of a substance (e.g. the mass or the number of moles) in a certain volume of a solution is called its concentration.

2) The more solute (the substance that's dissolved) there is in a given volume, the more concentrated the solution.

3) One way to measure the concentration of a solution is by calculating the mass of a substance in a given volume of solution. The units will be units of mass/units of volume. Here's how to calculate the concentration of a solution in $g/dm^3$:

$$\text{concentration} = \frac{\text{mass of solute}}{\text{volume of solvent}}$$

in $g/dm^3$ — mass of solute in g — volume of solvent in $dm^3$

**EXAMPLE:**

What's the concentration, in $g/dm^3$, of a solution of sodium chloride where 30 g of sodium chloride is dissolved in 0.2 $dm^3$ of water?

concentration $= \dfrac{30}{0.2} = 150$ $g/dm^3$     1 $dm^3 = 1000$ $cm^3$

4) You can calculate the mass of a solute in solution by rearranging the formula above to: mass = conc. × volume.

## Moles, mass, volume, concentration — don't get them muddled up

An important thing to take in here is that reactions are limited by the reactant which gets used up first. Once you've got that in the bag, keep practising until the calculations are an absolute breeze. Don't forget to learn the equation for finding the concentration of a solution and how to rearrange it.

# Warm-Up & Exam Questions

Think you know everything there is to about moles, limiting reactants and the volumes of gases?
Time to put that to the test with some questions...

## Warm-Up Questions

1) What do the numbers in front of the reactants and products
   in a balanced chemical equation stand for?

2) State why you might want to make sure one reactant
   is in excess when carrying out a chemical reaction.

3) In a reaction, what happens to the amount of product formed if the limiting reactant is halved?

4) What is meant by concentration?

## Exam Questions

**1**     3.5 g of Li reacts completely with 4 g of $O_2$ to produce 7.5 g of $Li_2O$.
$A_r(Li) = 7$, $M_r(O_2) = 32$, $M_r(Li_2O) = 30$.

**1.1**    Calculate how many moles of each substance reacted or was produced.

*[2 marks]*

**1.2**    Use your answer to part **1.1** to write a balanced symbol equation for this reaction.

*[2 marks]*

**2**     Sulfuric acid reacts with sodium hydrogen carbonate to produce aqueous sodium sulfate,
water and carbon dioxide. The balanced equation for this reaction is:

$$H_2SO_{4(aq)} + 2NaHCO_{3(s)} \rightarrow Na_2SO_{4(aq)} + 2H_2O_{(l)} + 2CO_{2(g)}$$

**2.1**    A student reacted 6.0 g of solid $NaHCO_3$ with an excess of sulfuric acid.
Calculate the theoretical yield of $Na_2SO_4$ for this reaction.

*[5 marks]*

**2.2**    Sodium hydrogen carbonate is the limiting reactant in the example in **2.1**.
Describe what is meant by the limiting reactant.

*[1 mark]*

**3**     A solution contains 24.5 g of solute in 160 $cm^3$ of solvent.

**3.1**    Calculate the concentration of the solution. Give your answer to 3 significant figures.

*[3 marks]*

**3.2**    A student needs to have 200 $cm^3$ of the same solution at a concentration of 75 $g/dm^3$.
How many grams of solute should she add to the solvent?

*[2 marks]*

**3.3**    At 25 °C the solubility of the solute is 56 kg per 100 $dm^3$.
Calculate the minimum volume in $dm^3$ (at 25 °C) needed to dissolve 640 g of the solute.
Give your answer to 3 significant figures.

*[4 marks]*

# Revision Summary for Topic 3

That wraps up Topic 3 — there's lots of equations and calculations in this section so practise is the name of the game. If you're unsure about anything have another read through before coming back to this page and putting your knowledge to the test with the questions below.

- Try these questions and tick off each one when you get it right.
- When you've done all the questions under a heading and are completely happy with it, tick it off.

## Relative Formula Mass (p.67) ☑

1) How do you calculate the relative formula mass, $M_r$ of a substance? ☑
2) How do you calculate the percentage mass of an element in a compound? ☑

## The Mole and Mass (p.68-70) ☑

3) State the value of the Avogadro constant. ☑
4) How many grams will 1 mole of the following substances weigh?
   a) C ☑
   b) $N_2$ ☑
   c) $CO_2$ ☑
5) What is the formula that relates the number of moles of a substance to its mass and $M_r$? ☑
6) What does conservation of mass mean? ☑
7) Suggest why the mass of a reaction vessel might decrease during a reaction. ☑

## The Mole and Concentration Equations (p.72-74) ☑

8) How can you determine the number of moles of each substance that would react together from the balanced reaction equation? ☑
9) What would increasing the limiting reagent do to the amount of product formed in a reaction? ☑
10) What is the yield of a reaction? ☑
11) Give the equation for working out the concentration of a solution in $g/dm^3$. ☑
12) Give the equation for working out the mass of solute added to a solution of known volume and concentration. ☑

## Acids and Bases

Acids and bases crop up everywhere in chemistry — so here's the lowdown on the basics of pH...

### The **pH Scale** Goes From **0 to 14**

1) The pH scale is a measure of how acidic or alkaline a solution is.

2) The lower the pH of a solution, the more acidic it is.
   The higher the pH of a solution, the more alkaline it is.

3) A neutral substance (e.g. pure water) has pH 7.

pH  0   1   2   3   4   5   6   7   8   9   10   11   12   13   14

← ACIDS | ALKALIS →

NEUTRAL

car battery acid, stomach acid | vinegar, lemon juice | acid rain | normal rain | pure water | washing-up liquid | pancreatic juice | soap powder | bleach | caustic soda (drain cleaner)

### You Can **Measure** the pH of a Solution

1) An indicator is a dye that changes colour depending on whether it's above or below a certain pH. Some indicators contain a mixture of dyes that means they gradually change colour over a broad range of pH. These are called wide range indicators and they're useful for estimating the pH of a solution. For example, universal indicator gives the colours shown above.

2) A pH probe attached to a pH meter can also be used to measure pH electronically. The probe is placed in the solution you are measuring and the pH is given on a digital display as a numerical value, meaning it's more accurate than an indicator.

### **Acids** and **Bases** Neutralise Each Other

1) An acid is a substance that forms an aqueous solution with a pH of less than 7. Acids form $H^+$ ions in water.

2) A base is any substance that will react with an acid to form a salt.

3) An alkali is a base that dissolves in water to form a solution with a pH greater than 7. Alkalis form $OH^-$ ions in water.

The reaction between acids and bases is called neutralisation:

$$acid + base \rightarrow salt + water$$

Neutralisation between acids and alkalis can be seen in terms of $H^+$ and $OH^-$ ions like this:

$$H^+_{(aq)} + OH^-_{(aq)} \rightarrow H_2O_{(l)}$$

Hydrogen ($H^+$) ions react with hydroxide ($OH^-$) ions to produce water.

When an acid neutralises a base (or vice versa), the products are neutral, i.e. they have a pH of 7. An indicator can be used to show that a neutralisation reaction is over.

### Interesting fact — your skin is slightly acidic (pH 5.5)

When you mix an acid with an alkali, hydrogen ions from the acid react with hydroxide ions from the alkali to make water. The leftover bits of the acid and alkali make a salt.

# Strong Acids, Weak Acids and their Reactions

Right, it's time for <u>strong acids</u> versus <u>weak acids</u>. Brace yourself, it's not the simplest bit of chemistry ever...

## Acids **Produce Protons** in **Water** ← *An $H^+$ ion is just a proton.*

The thing about acids is that they <u>ionise</u> in aqueous solution — they produce <u>hydrogen ions</u>, $H^+$.

For example:

$$HCl \rightarrow H^+ + Cl^-$$
$$HNO_3 \rightarrow H^+ + NO_3^-$$

*These acids don't produce hydrogen ions until they meet water. So, for example, hydrogen chloride gas isn't acidic.*

## Acids Can be **Strong** or **Weak**

1) <u>Strong acids</u> (e.g. sulfuric, hydrochloric and nitric acids) <u>ionise completely</u> in water. All the acid particles <u>dissociate</u> to release $H^+$ ions.

$$\underline{\text{Strong acid:}} \ HCl \longrightarrow H^+ + Cl^-$$

2) <u>Weak acids</u> (e.g. ethanoic, citric and carbonic acids) <u>do not fully ionise</u> in solution. Only a <u>small</u> proportion of acid particles dissociate to release $H^+$ ions.

3) The ionisation of a <u>weak</u> acid is a <u>reversible reaction</u>, which sets up an <u>equilibrium</u> between the <u>undissociated</u> and <u>dissociated acid</u>. Since only a few of the acid particles release $H^+$ ions, the position of <u>equilibrium</u> lies well to the <u>left</u>.

$$\underline{\text{Weak acid:}} \ CH_3COOH \rightleftharpoons H^+ + CH_3COO^-$$

*For more on equilibria turn to p.110.*

4) The <u>pH</u> of an acid or alkali is a measure of the <u>concentration</u> of $H^+$ ions in the solution.

5) For every <u>decrease</u> of 1 on the pH scale, the concentration of $H^+$ ions <u>increases</u> by a factor of <u>10</u>. So, an acid that has a pH of 4 has <u>10 times</u> the concentration of $H^+$ ions of an acid that has a pH of 5. For a <u>decrease</u> of 2 on the pH scale, the concentration of $H^+$ ions <u>increases</u> by a factor of <u>100</u>. The general rule for this is:

$$\text{Factor } H^+ \text{ ion concentration changes by} = 10^{-X}$$

*$X$ is the difference in pH, found by subtracting the starting pH from the final pH.*

**EXAMPLE:**

**During an experiment, the pH of a solution fell from pH 7 to pH 4. By what factor had the hydrogen ion concentration of the solution changed?**

Difference in pH = final pH − starting pH = 4 − 7 = −3.
Factor that $H^+$ ion concentration changed by = $10^{-(-3)} = 10^3$ (or 1000)

If the pH of the solution <u>increases</u>, the answer will be a decimal. For example if the pH of a solution increases by 1, the $H^+$ ion concentration changes by a factor of $10^{-1} = 0.1$. (This is the same as saying that the $H^+$ concentration has <u>decreased</u> by a factor of 10.)

6) The pH of a <u>strong</u> acid is always <u>lower</u> than the pH of a <u>weaker</u> acid if they have the <u>same concentration</u>.

## Strong acids ionise completely, but weak acids don't

Calculating the <u>factor</u> that <u>hydrogen ion concentration</u> changes by as <u>pH</u> changes can be a bit tricky. The best way to get to grips with it is just to get lots of <u>practice</u> at using the <u>formula</u>.

# Strong Acids, Weak Acids and their Reactions

## Don't Confuse **Strong** Acids with **Concentrated** Acids

1) Acid <u>strength</u> (i.e. strong or weak) tells you <u>what proportion</u> of the acid molecules <u>ionise</u> in water.

2) The <u>concentration</u> of an acid is different. Concentration measures <u>how much acid</u> there is in a certain volume of water. Concentration is basically how <u>watered down</u> your acid is.

*Concentration describes the <u>total number</u> of dissolved acid molecules — <u>not</u> the number of molecules that are ionised to produce hydrogen ions at any given moment.*

3) The larger the amount of acid there is in a certain volume of liquid, the <u>more concentrated</u> the acid is.

4) So you can have a <u>dilute</u> (not very concentrated) but <u>strong</u> acid, or a <u>concentrated but weak</u> acid.

5) pH will <u>decrease</u> with <u>increasing</u> acid concentration <u>regardless</u> of whether it's a strong <u>or</u> weak acid.

## Metal **Oxides** and Metal **Hydroxides** are **Bases**

1) Some <u>metal oxides</u> and <u>metal hydroxides</u> dissolve in <u>water</u>. These soluble compounds are <u>alkalis</u>. As you saw on page 77, alkalis react with acids in <u>neutralisation reactions</u>.

2) Even <u>bases</u> that <u>won't dissolve</u> in water will still take part in neutralisation reactions with acids.

3) So, all <u>metal oxides</u> and <u>metal hydroxides</u> react with <u>acids</u> to form a <u>salt</u> and <u>water</u>.

> Acid + Metal Oxide → Salt + Water

> Acid + Metal Hydroxide → Salt + Water

## The **Combination** of Metal and Acid Decides the **Salt**

This isn't exactly exciting, but it's pretty important, so try and get the hang of it:

| hydrochloric acid | + | copper oxide | → | copper chloride | + water |
| 2HCl | + | CuO | → | $CuCl_2$ | + $H_2O$ |
| hydrochloric acid | + | sodium hydroxide | → | sodium chloride | + water |
| HCl | + | NaOH | → | NaCl | + $H_2O$ |

| sulfuric acid | + | zinc oxide | → | zinc sulfate | + water |
| $H_2SO_4$ | + | ZnO | → | $ZnSO_4$ | + $H_2O$ |
| sulfuric acid | + | calcium hydroxide | → | calcium sulfate | + water |
| $H_2SO_4$ | + | $Ca(OH)_2$ | → | $CaSO_4$ | + $2H_2O$ |

*To work out the formula of an ionic compound, you need to balance the charges of the positive and negative ions so the compound is neutral. For more on formulas of ionic compounds, see p.50.*

| nitric acid | + | magnesium oxide | → | magnesium nitrate | + water |
| $2HNO_3$ | + | MgO | → | $Mg(NO_3)_2$ | + $H_2O$ |
| nitric acid | + | potassium hydroxide | → | potassium nitrate | + water |
| $HNO_3$ | + | KOH | → | $KNO_3$ | + $H_2O$ |

# Strong Acids, Weak Acids and their Reactions

## Acids and Metal **Carbonates** Produce **Carbon Dioxide**

Metal carbonates are also <u>bases</u>. They will react with acids to produce a salt, water and <u>carbon dioxide</u>.

> Acid + Metal Carbonate → Salt + Water + Carbon Dioxide

Here are a few examples of <u>acid</u> and <u>metal carbonate</u> reactions:

| hydrochloric acid | + | sodium carbonate | → | sodium chloride | + | water | + | carbon dioxide |
|---|---|---|---|---|---|---|---|---|
| $2HCl$ | + | $Na_2CO_3$ | → | $2NaCl$ | + | $H_2O$ | + | $CO_2$ |
| sulfuric acid | + | calcium carbonate | → | calcium sulfate | + | water | + | carbon dioxide |
| $H_2SO_4$ | + | $CaCO_3$ | → | $CaSO_4$ | + | $H_2O$ | + | $CO_2$ |

## You can Make **Soluble Salts** Using an **Insoluble Base**

1) You need to pick the right <u>acid</u>, plus an <u>insoluble base</u> such as an <u>insoluble hydroxide</u>, <u>metal oxide</u> or <u>carbonate</u>.

*You can also make some salts by reacting a metal with an acid (see page 83 for more).*

For example, if you want to make <u>copper chloride</u>, you could mix <u>hydrochloric acid</u> and <u>copper oxide</u>:   $CuO_{(s)} + 2HCl_{(aq)} \rightarrow CuCl_{2\,(aq)} + H_2O_{(l)}$

2) Gently warm the dilute acid using a Bunsen burner, then turn off the Bunsen burner.

3) Add the <u>insoluble base</u> to the <u>acid</u> a bit at a time until no more reacts (i.e. the base is in <u>excess</u>). You'll know when all the acid has been neutralised because, even after stirring, the excess solid will just <u>sink</u> to the bottom of the flask.

4) Then <u>filter</u> out the <u>excess</u> solid to get the salt solution (see p.26).

5) To get <u>pure</u>, <u>solid</u> crystals of the <u>salt</u>, gently heat the solution using a <u>water bath</u> or an <u>electric heater</u> to evaporate some of the water (to make it more concentrated) and then stop heating it and leave the solution to cool. <u>Crystals</u> of the salt should form, which can be <u>filtered</u> out of the solution and then <u>dried</u>. This is called <u>crystallisation</u> (see p.26).

filter paper

filter funnel

## Quite a few reactions to learn here...

...but it's not so bad really, because they're all <u>acid</u> + <u>base</u> → <u>salt</u> + <u>water</u> (and sometimes <u>carbon dioxide</u>). Remember, you could be asked to describe how you would make a pure, dry sample of a given <u>soluble salt</u>, so make sure you understand the <u>method</u> and that you could suggest a suitable <u>acid</u> and <u>base</u> to use.

# Warm-Up & Exam Questions

So you think you know everything there is to know about acids?  Time to put yourself to the test.

## Warm-Up Questions

1) What range of values can pH take?
2) What term is used to describe a solution with a pH of 7?
3) What's the difference between a strong acid and a weak acid?
4) If the pH of the solution rises from 2 to 5, what factor has the hydrogen ion concentration of the solution changed by?
5) Name the two substances formed when nitric acid reacts with copper hydroxide.

## Exam Questions

**1**    A student had a sample of acid in a test tube.  He gradually added some alkali to the acid. *(Grade 4-6)*

**1.1**    Name the type of ion that acids produce in aqueous solutions.

*[1 mark]*

**1.2**    What type of reaction took place in the student's experiment?  Tick **one** box.

☐ thermal decomposition          ☐ redox

☐ neutralisation          ☐ combustion

*[1 mark]*

**2**    All metal hydroxides are bases.  They can react with acids to form a salt and water. *(Grade 6-7)*

**2.1**    Sodium hydroxide is a soluble base.  What name is given to bases that dissolve in water?

*[1 mark]*

**2.2**    Complete and balance the symbol equation given below for the reaction of nitric acid with magnesium hydroxide.

$$2HNO_3 + Mg(OH)_2 \rightarrow \text{.........................} + \text{.........................}$$

*[2 marks]*

**PRACTICAL**

**3**    Silver nitrate is a soluble salt.  It can be made by adding an excess of insoluble silver carbonate to nitric acid until no further reaction occurs. *(Grade 6-7)*

**Figure 1**

**3.1**    Give **one** observation that would indicate that the reaction is complete.

*[1 mark]*

**3.2**    Once the reaction is complete, the excess silver carbonate can be separated from the silver nitrate solution using the apparatus shown in **Figure 1**.  What is this method of separation called?

*[1 mark]*

**3.3**    Describe how you could produce solid silver nitrate from silver nitrate solution.

*[3 marks]*

# Metals and their Reactivity

Metals can be placed in order of <u>reactivity</u>. This can be really useful for <u>predicting</u> their <u>reactions</u>.

## The **Reactivity Series** — How Well a **Metal** Reacts

1) The <u>reactivity series</u> lists metals in <u>order</u> of their <u>reactivity</u> towards other substances.

2) For metals, their reactivity is determined by how <u>easily</u> they lose electrons — forming positive ions. The <u>higher</u> up the reactivity series a metal is, the more easily it will form <u>positive ions</u>.

3) When metals <u>react</u> with <u>water</u> or <u>acid</u>, they <u>lose</u> electrons and form positive ions. So, the <u>higher</u> a metal is in the reactivity series, the more <u>easily</u> it <u>reacts</u> with water or acid.

4) If you <u>compare</u> the relative reactivity of different metals with either an <u>acid</u> or <u>water</u> and put them in order from the <u>most</u> reactive to the <u>least</u> reactive, the order you get is the reactivity series.

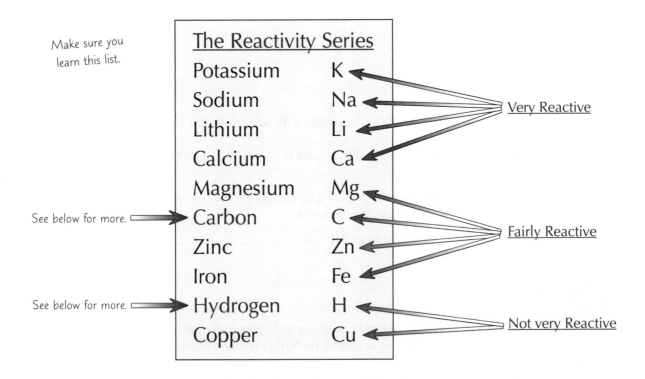

Make sure you learn this list.

The Reactivity Series

| Potassium | K | Very Reactive |
| Sodium | Na | |
| Lithium | Li | |
| Calcium | Ca | |
| Magnesium | Mg | Fairly Reactive |
| Carbon | C | |
| Zinc | Zn | |
| Iron | Fe | |
| Hydrogen | H | Not very Reactive |
| Copper | Cu | |

See below for more. → Carbon

See below for more. → Hydrogen

## Carbon and Hydrogen

<u>Carbon</u> and <u>hydrogen</u> are non-metals, but they're often included in the reactivity series, because this gives you information about how metals will react with them:

- Metals that are <u>less reactive</u> than carbon <u>can</u> be extracted from their ores by reduction with <u>carbon</u> (see p.84). Metals that are <u>more reactive</u> than carbon <u>cannot</u> be extracted in this way.
- Metals that are <u>more reactive</u> than hydrogen (<u>above</u> it in the reactivity series) <u>will</u> react with <u>acids</u>. Metals <u>less reactive</u> than hydrogen <u>will not</u> react with <u>acids</u>.

# Metals and their Reactivity

## How **Metals** React With **Acids** Tells You About Their **Reactivity**

Some metals react with acids to produce a <u>salt</u> and <u>hydrogen gas</u>.

$$\text{Acid } + \text{ Metal } \rightarrow \text{ Salt } + \text{ Hydrogen}$$

Hydrochloric acid will react to form chloride salts and sulfuric acid will react to form sulfate salts.

1)  The <u>speed</u> of reaction is indicated by the <u>rate</u> at which the <u>bubbles</u> of hydrogen are given off.

2)  The more <u>reactive</u> the metal, the <u>faster</u> the reaction will go. Very reactive metals like potassium, sodium, lithium and calcium react explosively, but less reactive metals such as magnesium, zinc and iron react less violently. In general, copper <u>won't</u> react with cold, dilute acids.

Magnesium reacts <u>vigorously</u> with <u>cold</u> dilute acids like $HCl_{(aq)}$ and $H_2SO_{4(aq)}$ and produces <u>loads of bubbles</u>.

Both zinc and iron react fairly <u>slowly</u> with dilute acids, but more strongly if you heat them up.

Dilute Acid

Dilute Acid

Dilute Acid

magnesium

zinc

iron

$Mg_{(s)} + 2HCl_{(aq)} \rightarrow MgCl_{2(aq)} + H_{2(g)}$    $Zn_{(s)} + 2HCl_{(aq)} \rightarrow ZnCl_{2(aq)} + H_{2(g)}$    $Fe_{(s)} + 2HCl_{(aq)} \rightarrow FeCl_{2(aq)} + H_{2(g)}$

$Mg_{(s)} + H_2SO_{4(aq)} \rightarrow MgSO_{4(aq)} + H_{2(g)}$    $Zn_{(s)} + H_2SO_{4(aq)} \rightarrow ZnSO_{4(aq)} + H_{2(g)}$    $Fe_{(s)} + H_2SO_{4(aq)} \rightarrow FeSO_{4(aq)} + H_{2(g)}$

You can use the <u>burning splint test</u> (see page 123) to confirm that <u>hydrogen</u> is formed in these reactions.

## Metals Also React with **Water**

The <u>reactions</u> of metals with <u>water</u> also show the reactivity of metals.

$$\text{Metal} + \text{Water} \rightarrow \text{Metal Hydroxide} + \text{Hydrogen}$$

For example, calcium:    $Ca_{(s)} + 2H_2O_{(l)} \rightarrow Ca(OH)_{2(aq)} + H_{2(g)}$

You can see more on the reactions of Group 1 metals with water on page 39.

1)  The metals <u>potassium</u>, <u>sodium</u>, <u>lithium</u> and <u>calcium</u> will all react with water.

2)  Less reactive metals like <u>zinc</u>, <u>iron</u> and <u>copper</u> won't react with water.

## Metals at the top of the reactivity series are highly reactive

You can use the results of experiments like these to work out an <u>order of reactivity</u> for the metals that you used. Just remember, the <u>more vigorous</u> the reaction with acid or water, the <u>more reactive</u> the metal.

# Metals and their Reactivity

## Metals Often Have to be Separated from their **Oxides**

1) Most metals aren't found in the earth in their <u>pure</u> form.  They tend to be fairly reactive, so they're usually found as <u>compounds</u> and have to be <u>extracted</u> before they can be used.

2) Lots of common metals, like iron and aluminium, react with <u>oxygen</u> to form their <u>oxides</u>, which are found in the ground.  This process is an example of <u>oxidation</u>. These oxides are often the <u>ores</u> that the metals need to be extracted from.

*An ore is a type of rock that contains metal compounds.*

3) A reaction that separates a metal from its oxide is called a <u>reduction reaction</u>.

### Formation of Metal Ore:

**Oxidation = Gain of Oxygen**

For example, magnesium can be <u>oxidised</u> to make magnesium oxide.

$$2Mg + O_2 \rightarrow 2MgO$$

### Extraction of Metal:

**Reduction = Loss of Oxygen**

For example, copper oxide can be <u>reduced</u> to copper.

$$2CuO + C \rightarrow 2Cu + CO_2$$

## Some Metals can be **Extracted** by **Reduction** with **Carbon**

1) Some metals can be <u>extracted</u> from their ores chemically by <u>reduction</u> using <u>carbon</u>.

2) In this reaction, the ore is <u>reduced</u> as oxygen is <u>removed</u> from it, and carbon <u>gains</u> oxygen so is <u>oxidised</u>.

For example:

| $2Fe_2O_3$ | + | $3C$ | $\rightarrow$ | $4Fe$ | + | $3CO_2$ |
|---|---|---|---|---|---|---|
| iron(III) oxide | + | carbon | $\rightarrow$ | iron | + | carbon dioxide |

3) As you saw on p.82, the position of the metal in the <u>reactivity series</u> determines whether it can be extracted by <u>reduction</u> with carbon.

- Metals <u>higher than carbon</u> in the reactivity series have to be extracted using <u>electrolysis</u>, which is expensive.

- Metals <u>below carbon</u> in the reactivity series can be extracted by <u>reduction</u> using <u>carbon</u>.  For example, <u>iron oxide</u> is reduced in a <u>blast furnace</u> to make <u>iron</u>.  This is because carbon <u>can only take the oxygen</u> away from metals which are <u>less reactive</u> than carbon <u>itself</u> is.

The Reactivity Series

| | | |
|---|---|---|
| Potassium | K | more reactive |
| Sodium | Na | |
| Lithium | Li | |
| Calcium | Ca | |
| Magnesium | Mg | |
| CARBON | C | |
| Zinc | Zn | |
| Iron | Fe | |
| Hydrogen | H | |
| Copper | Cu | less reactive |

Extracted by using <u>electrolysis</u>.

Extracted by <u>reduction</u> with <u>carbon</u>.

A few metals are <u>so unreactive</u> that they are found in the earth as the metal <u>itself</u>.  For example, <u>gold</u> is mined as its elemental form.

## Carbon can't reduce things that are above it in the reactivity series

Make sure you understand the difference between <u>reduction</u> and <u>oxidation</u> and make sure that you can spot which substance has been <u>reduced</u> and which substance has been <u>oxidised</u> in a reaction.

# Redox Reactions

Reduction and oxidation <u>doesn't</u> just mean the loss or gain of oxygen — it can also refer to <u>electron</u> transfer.

## If **Electrons** are **Transferred**, it's a **Redox Reaction**

Oxidation can mean the <u>addition of oxygen</u> (or a reaction with it), and reduction can be the <u>removal of oxygen</u>. But you can also define oxidation and reduction in terms of <u>electrons</u>:

> A loss of electrons is called oxidation.

> A gain of electrons is called reduction.

*Make sure you learn these definitions.*

A handy way to remember this is using the mnemonic <u>OIL RIG</u>:

> <u>O</u>xidation <u>I</u>s <u>L</u>oss, <u>R</u>eduction <u>I</u>s <u>G</u>ain    (of <u>electrons</u>)

<u>RED</u>uction and <u>OX</u>idation happen <u>at the same time</u> — hence the name "<u>REDOX</u>".

## Some **Examples** of **Redox Reactions:**

### Metals reacting with acids

1) All reactions of <u>metals</u> with <u>acids</u> (see page 83) are <u>redox reactions</u>.

2) For example, the reaction of <u>iron</u> with <u>dilute sulfuric acid</u> is a redox reaction.

3) The <u>iron atoms lose electrons</u> to become iron(II) ions — they are <u>oxidised</u> by the hydrogen ions.

$$Fe \rightarrow Fe^{2+} + 2e^-$$

4) The <u>hydrogen ions gain electrons</u> to become hydrogen atoms — they are <u>reduced</u> by the iron atoms.

$$2H^+ + 2e^- \rightarrow H_2$$

5) The ionic equation (see page 86) for the redox reaction is: $Fe + 2H^+ \rightarrow Fe^{2+} + H_2$

*Ionic equations only show the things that are actually reacting — the sulfate ions from the acid aren't shown here, because nothing happens to them.*

### Halogen Displacement Reactions

1) A more reactive halogen can displace a less reactive halogen from a salt solution (see page 41).

2) For example, chlorine can displace bromine from potassium bromide solution.

3) The <u>chlorine atoms gain electrons</u> to become chloride ions — they are <u>reduced</u> by the bromide ions.

$$Cl_2 + 2e^- \rightarrow 2Cl^-$$

4) The <u>bromide ions lose electrons</u> to become bromine atoms — they are <u>oxidised</u> by the chlorine atoms.

$$2Br^- \rightarrow Br_2 + 2e^-$$

5) The ionic equation for this redox reaction is: $Cl_2 + 2Br^- \rightarrow 2Cl^- + Br_2$

*Same here — the ionic equation doesn't show the potassium ions from the potassium bromide, because nothing happens to them.*

## Remember OIL RIG — 'Oxidation Is Loss, Reduction Is Gain'

<u>OIL RIG</u> is a pretty handy way of reminding yourself about what goes on during a <u>redox reaction</u>. Make sure that you don't forget that redox reactions are all about the <u>transfer of electrons</u>.

# Redox Reactions

## Metal Displacement Reactions are Redox Reactions

1) If you put a <u>reactive metal</u> into the solution of a <u>dissolved metal compound</u>, the reactive metal will <u>replace</u> the <u>less reactive metal</u> in the compound (see the reactivity series on page 82).

2) This type of reaction is another example of a <u>displacement</u> reaction.

3) Here's the rule to remember:

> A <u>MORE REACTIVE</u> metal will displace a <u>LESS REACTIVE</u> metal from its compound.

For example, if you put <u>iron</u> in a solution of <u>copper sulfate</u> ($CuSO_4$) the more reactive iron will "<u>kick out</u>" the less reactive copper from the solution. You end up with <u>iron sulfate</u> solution ($FeSO_4$) and <u>copper metal</u>:

$$\text{iron + copper sulfate} \rightarrow \text{iron sulfate + copper}$$
$$Fe_{(s)} + CuSO_{4(aq)} \rightarrow FeSO_{4(aq)} + Cu_{(s)}$$

In this reaction the iron <u>loses</u> 2 electrons to become a 2+ ion — it's <u>oxidised</u>.

$$Fe \rightarrow Fe^{2+} + 2e^-$$

The copper ion <u>gains</u> these 2 electrons to become a copper atom — it's <u>reduced</u>.

$$Cu^{2+} + 2e^- \rightarrow Cu$$

This reaction is used in industry to produce pure copper from copper salt solutions and cheap scrap iron.

3) In metal displacement reactions it's always the metal <u>ion</u> that gains electrons and is <u>reduced</u>. The metal <u>atom</u> always loses electrons and is <u>oxidised</u>.

4) In the exam you could be asked to write <u>word or symbol equations</u> for metal displacement reactions.

## Ionic Equations Show Just the Useful Bits of Reactions

1) In an <u>ionic equation</u> only the particles that react and the products they form are shown. For example:

$$Mg_{(s)} + Zn^{2+}_{(aq)} \rightarrow Mg^{2+}_{(aq)} + Zn_{(s)}$$

2) This <u>just</u> shows the <u>displacement</u> of <u>zinc ions</u> by magnesium metal. Here's what the full equation of the above reaction would be if you'd started off with magnesium metal and zinc chloride solution:

$$Mg_{(s)} + ZnCl_{2(aq)} \rightarrow MgCl_{2(aq)} + Zn_{(s)}$$

3) If you write out the equation so you can see all the ions, you'll see that the chloride ions <u>don't change</u> in the reaction — they're <u>spectator ions</u>.

$$Mg_{(s)} + Zn^{2+}_{(aq)} + 2Cl^-_{(aq)} \rightarrow Mg^{2+}_{(aq)} + 2Cl^-_{(aq)} + Zn_{(s)}$$

4) You don't include spectator ions in the ionic equation, so to get from this to the ionic equation, you cross out the chloride ions.

5) The ionic equation just <u>concentrates</u> on the substances which are <u>oxidised</u> or <u>reduced</u>.

## A displacement reaction is a type of redox reaction

Try writing some <u>ionic equations</u> now — write the ionic equation for the reaction between <u>zinc</u> and <u>iron chloride</u> ($FeCl_2$). What's being <u>oxidised</u>? What's being <u>reduced</u>?

# Warm-Up & Exam Questions

Hoping to test your knowledge with some testing chemistry questions? You're in luck...

## Warm-Up Questions

1) What determines the reactivity of a metal?
2) Magnesium is reacted with dilute hydrochloric acid. Give the name of the salt formed.
3) Which two substances are formed when a metal reacts with water?
4) This equation shows how zinc reacts with copper chloride: $Zn_{(s)} + CuCl_{2(aq)} \rightarrow ZnCl_{2(aq)} + Cu_{(s)}$
   a) Write an ionic equation for this reaction.
   b) State which species in this reaction is being oxidised.

## Exam Questions

**1**    **Figure 1** shows part of the reactivity series of metals.  Hydrogen has also been included in this reactivity series.

**Figure 1**

| Potassium K |
| Sodium Na |
| Calcium Ca |
| Magnesium Mg |
| Zinc Zn |
| Iron Fe |
| HYDROGEN H |
| Copper Cu |

**1.1**    Name **one** metal from **Figure 1** that is more reactive than magnesium.

*[1 mark]*

**1.2**    Name **one** metal from **Figure 1** which would not react with acids at all.

*[1 mark]*

**1.3**    A student places a small piece of zinc into dilute acid. The mixture produces bubbles of hydrogen gas fairly slowly. Use this information to predict what would happen if the student repeated the experiment using iron.

*[2 marks]*

**2**    Iron can be extracted by the reduction of iron(III) oxide ($Fe_2O_3$)  with carbon (C), to produce iron and carbon dioxide.

**2.1**    Write a balanced symbol equation for this reaction.

*[2 marks]*

**2.2**    Explain why the iron(III) oxide is described as being reduced during this reaction.

*[1 mark]*

**3**    A student adds a piece of copper to some iron sulfate solution and a piece of iron to some copper sulfate solution. **Figure 2** shows what the test tubes looked like just after he added the metals. Predict what he will observe in both tubes, **A** and **B**, after 2 hours. Explain your answer.

**Figure 2**

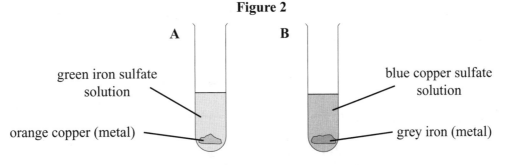

*[6 marks]*

# Electrolysis

You need to know the ins and outs of how <u>electrolysis</u> works.  So buckle up, here we go...

## Electrolysis Means 'Splitting Up with Electricity'

1) During electrolysis, an electric current is passed through an <u>electrolyte</u>.  The electrolyte is a <u>molten</u> or <u>dissolved</u> ionic compound (it must be molten or dissolved so that the ions are free to <u>move</u>).

2) The ions move towards the electrodes, where they react, and the compound <u>decomposes</u>.

3) The <u>positive ions</u> in the electrolyte will move towards the <u>cathode</u> (–ve electrode) and <u>gain</u> electrons (they are <u>reduced</u>).

4) The <u>negative ions</u> in the electrolyte will move towards the <u>anode</u> (+ve electrode) and <u>lose</u> electrons (they are <u>oxidised</u>).

> An electrolyte is just a liquid or solution that can conduct electricity. An electrode is a solid that conducts electricity and is submerged in the electrolyte.

5) This creates a <u>flow of charge</u> through the <u>electrolyte</u> as ions travel to the electrodes.

6) As ions gain or lose electrons, they form the uncharged element and are <u>discharged</u> from the electrolyte.

## Electrolysis of Molten Ionic Solids Forms Elements

1) An <u>ionic solid can't</u> be electrolysed because the ions are in fixed positions and <u>can't move</u>.

2) <u>Molten ionic compounds can</u> be electrolysed because the ions can <u>move freely</u> and conduct electricity.

3) Molten ionic compounds are always broken up into their <u>elements</u>. A good example of this is the electrolysis of <u>molten lead bromide</u>:

4) The electrodes should be made of an <u>inert</u> material, so they <u>don't react</u> with the electrolyte.

5) Positive <u>metal</u> ions are <u>reduced</u> to the element at the <u>cathode</u>:

$$Pb^{2+} + 2e^- \rightarrow Pb$$

6) Negative <u>non-metal</u> ions are <u>oxidised</u> to the element at the <u>anode</u>:

$$2Br^- \rightarrow Br_2 + 2e^-$$

> Both of these equations are half equations.  For more on half equations have a look at page 91.

# Electrolysis

## Metals can be **Extracted** From Their **Ores** Using **Electrolysis**

If a metal is <u>too reactive</u> to be <u>reduced</u> with <u>carbon</u> (page 84) or reacts with carbon, then electrolysis can be used to extract it. Extracting metals via this method is <u>very expensive</u> as <u>lots of energy</u> is required to melt the ore and produce the required current. For example:

1) Aluminium is extracted from the ore <u>bauxite</u> by <u>electrolysis</u>.
Bauxite contains <u>aluminium oxide</u>, $Al_2O_3$.

2) Aluminium oxide has a <u>very high</u> melting temperature so it's mixed with <u>cryolite</u> to lower the melting point.

*Cryolite is an aluminium based compound with a lower melting point than aluminium oxide.*

3) The <u>molten mixture</u> contains <u>free ions</u> — so it'll <u>conduct electricity</u>.

4) The <u>positive $Al^{3+}$ ions</u> are attracted to the <u>negative electrode</u> where they <u>each pick up three electrons</u> and turn into neutral <u>aluminium atoms</u>. These then <u>sink</u> to the bottom of the electrolysis tank.

5) The <u>negative $O^{2-}$ ions</u> are attracted to the <u>positive electrode</u> where they <u>each lose two electrons</u>. The neutral oxygen atoms will then <u>combine</u> to form <u>$O_2$</u> molecules.

*The anode is made of carbon and needs to be replaced regularly as it reacts with oxygen to produce carbon dioxide.*

## At the **Negative** Electrode:

1) <u>Metals</u> form <u>positive ions</u>, so they're attracted to the <u>negative</u> electrode.

2) So <u>aluminium</u> is produced at the <u>negative electrode</u>:

$$Al^{3+} + 3e^- \rightarrow Al$$

*This is <u>reduction</u> — a gain of electrons.*

## At the **Positive** Electrode:

1) <u>Non-metals</u> form <u>negative ions</u>, so they're attracted to the positive electrode.

2) So <u>oxygen</u> is produced at the <u>positive electrode</u>:

$$2O^{2-} \rightarrow O_2 + 4e^-$$

*This is <u>oxidation</u> — a loss of electrons.*

## **Overall** Equation:

aluminium oxide $\rightarrow$ aluminium + oxygen
$$2Al_2O_{3(l)} \rightarrow 4Al_{(l)} + 3O_{2(g)}$$

# Electrolysis of Aqueous Solutions

When carrying out <u>electrolysis</u> on an <u>aqueous solution</u> you have to factor in the ions in <u>water</u>.

## It May be Easier to **Discharge Ions** from **Water** than the **Solute**

1) In <u>aqueous solutions</u>, as well as the <u>ions</u> from the ionic compound, there will be <u>hydrogen ions</u> ($H^+$) and <u>hydroxide ions</u> ($OH^-$) from the <u>water</u>: $H_2O_{(l)} \rightleftharpoons H^+_{(aq)} + OH^-_{(aq)}$

2) Which ions are discharged at the electrodes when the solution is electrolysed will depend on the <u>relative reactivity</u> of all the ions in the solution.

### Cathode

- At the <u>cathode</u>, if <u>$H^+$ ions and metal ions</u> are present, <u>hydrogen gas</u> will be produced if the metal ions form an elemental metal that is <u>more reactive</u> than hydrogen (e.g. sodium ions).
- If the metal ions form an elemental metal that is <u>less reactive</u> than hydrogen (e.g. copper ions), a solid layer of the <u>pure metal</u> will be produced instead, which will <u>coat</u> the cathode.

### Anode

- At the anode, if <u>$OH^-$ and halide ions</u> ($Cl^-$, $Br^-$, $I^-$) are present, molecules of chlorine, bromine or iodine will be formed.
- If <u>no halide ions</u> are present, then the $OH^-$ ions from the water will be discharged and <u>oxygen gas</u> (and <u>water</u>) will be formed.

## Example 1: Electrolysis of **Copper Sulfate Solution**

A solution of <u>copper(II) sulfate</u> ($CuSO_4$) contains <u>four different ions</u>: $Cu^{2+}$, $SO_4^{2-}$, $H^+$ and $OH^-$.

<u>Copper</u> metal is less reactive than hydrogen, so at the cathode <u>copper metal</u> is produced and coats the electrode:

$$Cu^{2+} + 2e^- \rightarrow Cu$$

There aren't any <u>halide ions</u> present, so at the anode <u>oxygen</u> and <u>water</u> are produced: The oxygen can be seen as <u>bubbles</u>.

$$4OH^- \rightarrow O_2 + 2H_2O + 4e^-$$

# Electrolysis of Aqueous Solutions

## Example 2: Electrolysis of **Sodium Chloride Solution**

A solution of <u>sodium chloride</u> (NaCl) contains <u>four different ions</u>: $Na^+$, $Cl^-$, $OH^-$ and $H^+$.

<u>Sodium</u> metal is more reactive than hydrogen. So at the cathode, <u>hydrogen gas</u> is produced.

$$2H^+ + 2e^- \rightarrow H_2$$

<u>Chloride ions</u> are present in the solution. So at the anode <u>chlorine gas</u> is produced.

$$2Cl^- \rightarrow Cl_2 + 2e^-$$

d.c. power supply

cathode (−ve)

anode (+ve)

bubbles of hydrogen gas

bubbles of pale green chlorine gas

NaCl solution

You can do an electrolysis <u>experiment</u> in the <u>lab</u> using a set-up like the one on page 153. Once the experiment is finished you can <u>test</u> any <u>gaseous products</u> to work out what has been produced at the electrodes:

PRACTICAL

- Chlorine <u>bleaches</u> damp <u>litmus paper</u>, turning it white.
- Hydrogen makes a "<u>squeaky pop</u>" with a <u>lighted splint</u>.
- Oxygen will <u>relight</u> a <u>glowing splint</u>.

*For more on tests for gases,* *turn to page 123.*

## The **Half Equations** — Make Sure **the Electrons Balance**

1) <u>Half equations</u> show the reactions at the <u>electrodes</u> (they show ions or atoms <u>gaining</u> or <u>losing electrons</u>).

2) You can <u>combine</u> the half equations for the reactions at both electrodes to get the <u>ionic equation</u> for the <u>overall reaction</u>. The important thing to remember when you combine half equations is that the <u>number of electrons</u> shown in each half equation <u>must be the same</u>.

For the electrolysis of <u>aqueous sodium chloride solution</u> the half equations are:
<u>Negative Electrode</u>: $2H^+ + 2e^- \rightarrow H_2$
<u>Positive Electrode</u>: $2Cl^- \rightarrow Cl_2 + 2e^-$ (or $2Cl^- - 2e^- \rightarrow Cl_2$)
You can combine these to get the <u>ionic equation</u>: $\mathbf{2H^+ + 2Cl^- \rightarrow H_2 + Cl_2}$

*The electrons on each side of the half equations balance, so they cancel out in the full ionic equation.*

Remember, if there are <u>no halide ions</u> in an aqueous solution, $OH^-$ ions are discharged at the positive electrode. The half equation for this is: $4OH^- \rightarrow O_2 + 2H_2O + 4e^-$ (or $4OH^- - 4e^- \rightarrow O_2 + 2H_2O$)

## Remember — all aqueous solutions contain OH⁻ and H⁺ ions

The main points to remember about the <u>electrolysis</u> of <u>aqueous solutions</u> are: 1) At the <u>cathode</u>, <u>hydrogen</u> gas is made, <u>unless</u> the metal ions are <u>less reactive</u> than hydrogen — then you get a coating of the <u>metal</u>. 2) At the <u>anode</u>, <u>oxygen</u> and <u>water</u> are made, <u>unless</u> halide ions are present — then the <u>halogen</u> is made.

# Warm-Up & Exam Questions

Time to test your mettle. Try and get through the following questions. If there's anything you're not quite sure about, have a look at the pages again until you can answer the questions without batting an eyelid.

## Warm-Up Questions

1) At which electrode are metals deposited during electrolysis?
2) What products are made when molten zinc chloride is electrolysed?
3) During the electrolysis of molten aluminium oxide are the aluminium ions being reduced or oxidised?
4) What is formed at the cathode during the electrolysis of an aqueous solution of potassium hydroxide?

## Exam Questions

**1**  Aluminium is extracted by electrolysis of molten aluminium oxide ($Al_2O_3$).  *Grade 6-7*

**1.1**  The aluminium oxide is dissolved in molten cryolite. State why.

*[1 mark]*

**1.2**  Complete the half equation below for the reaction that occurs at the negative electrode.

$$\text{................} + 3e^- \rightarrow \text{..................}$$

*[1 mark]*

**1.3**  Complete the half equation below for the reaction that occurs at the positive electrode.

$$\text{................} \rightarrow \text{..................} + 4e^-$$

*[1 mark]*

**1.4**  The positive electrode is made of carbon. Explain why it will need to be replaced over time.

*[2 marks]*

**2**  When sodium solution chloride is electrolysed, a gas is produced at each electrode.  *Grade 6-7*

**2.1**  Name the gas produced at the negative electrode.

*[1 mark]*

**2.2**  Give the half equation for the reaction at the negative electrode.

*[1 mark]*

**2.3**  Name the gas produced at the positive electrode.

*[1 mark]*

**2.4**  Give the half equation for the reaction at the positive electrode.

*[1 mark]*

**2.5**  Explain why sodium hydroxide is left in solution at the end of the reaction.

*[2 marks]*

**2.6**  If copper chloride solution is electrolysed, copper metal is produced at the negative electrode, instead of the gas named in **2.1**. Explain why.

*[1 mark]*

# Revision Summary for Topic 4

That wraps up Topic 4 — time to put yourself to the test and find out how much you really know.
- Try these questions and tick off each one when you get it right.
- When you've done all the questions under a heading and are completely happy with it, tick it off.

## Acids and their Reactions (p.77-80) ☑

1) State whether the following pH values are acidic, alkaline or neutral.
   a) 9          b) 2          c) 7          d) 6          ☑

2) Give the general word equation for the reaction between an acid and a base. ☑

3) What is a strong acid? ☑

4) By what factor does the $H^+$ concentration increase for a decrease of 1 on the pH scale? ☑

5) Explain the difference between a strong acid and a concentrated one. ☑

6) Write a balanced equation for the reaction between hydrochloric acid and sodium carbonate. ☑

## Reactivity of Metals and Redox Reactions (p.82-86) ☑

7) Is zinc more or less reactive than iron? ☑

8) What is the general word equation for the reaction of a metal with an acid? ☑

9) Give the balanced equation for the reaction of calcium with water. ☑

10) Will copper react with water? ☑

11) What product is formed when magnesium is oxidised by oxygen? ☑

12) Explain how you can use a reactivity series to work out whether or not
    it is possible to extract a metal from its oxide by reduction with carbon. ☑

13) Why is gold found as a pure metal in the earth? ☑

14) In terms of electrons, give the definition of oxidation. ☑

15) In a displacement reaction, does the metal atom get reduced or oxidised? ☑

## Electrolysis (p.88-91) ☑

16) During electrolysis, which electrode are the positive ions attracted to? ☑

17) Why can ionic solids not undergo electrolysis? ☑

18) During electrolysis, do ions get reduced or oxidised at the anode? ☑

19) During the manufacture of aluminium from bauxite, which electrode is aluminium formed at? ☑

20) In what situation will hydrogen gas be given out during
    the electrolysis of an aqueous solution of an ionic solid? ☑

21) If halide ions are present in an aqueous solution of an ionic solid,
    will oxygen gas be released when the solution is electrolysed? ☑

22) What test could you use to determine if hydrogen gas
    has been produced in an electrolysis reaction? ☑

# Exothermic and Endothermic Reactions

Whenever chemical reactions occur, there are changes in <u>energy</u>. This means that when chemicals get together, things either <u>heat up</u> or <u>cool down</u>. I'll give you a heads up — this page is a good 'un.

## Energy is **Moved Around** in **Chemical Reactions**

1) Chemicals <u>store</u> a certain amount of energy — and <u>different chemicals</u> store <u>different amounts</u>.

2) If the <u>products</u> of a reaction store <u>more</u> energy than the <u>original reactants</u>, then they must have <u>taken in</u> the difference in energy between the products and reactants from the <u>surroundings</u> during the reaction.

3) But if they store <u>less</u>, then the <u>excess</u> energy was transferred <u>to the surroundings</u> during the reaction.

4) The <u>overall</u> amount of energy doesn't change. This is because energy is <u>conserved</u> in reactions — it can't be created or destroyed, only <u>moved around</u>. This means the amount of energy in the <u>universe</u> always stays the <u>same</u>.

## In an **Exothermic** Reaction, Heat is **Given Out**

> An <u>exothermic</u> reaction is one which <u>transfers</u> energy to the <u>surroundings</u>, usually by <u>heating</u>. This is shown by a <u>rise in temperature</u>.

1) The best example of an exothermic reaction is <u>burning fuels</u> — also called <u>combustion</u>. This gives out a lot of energy — it's very exothermic.

2) <u>Neutralisation reactions</u> (acid + alkali) are also exothermic.

3) Many <u>oxidation reactions</u> are exothermic. For example, adding sodium to water <u>releases energy</u>, so it must be exothermic — see page 39. The reaction <u>releases energy</u> and the sodium moves about on the surface of the water as it is oxidised.

4) Exothermic reactions have lots of everyday uses. For example:

> - Some <u>hand warmers</u> use the exothermic oxidation of <u>iron</u> in air (with a salt solution catalyst) to <u>release energy</u>.
> - <u>Self heating cans</u> of hot chocolate and coffee also rely on <u>exothermic reactions</u> between chemicals in their bases.

## In an **Endothermic** Reaction, Heat is **Taken In**

*Physical processes can also take in or release energy. E.g. freezing is an exothermic process, melting is endothermic.*

> An <u>endothermic</u> reaction is one which <u>takes in</u> energy <u>from</u> the surroundings. This is shown by a <u>fall in temperature</u>.

1) Endothermic reactions are much <u>less common</u> than exothermic reactions, but they include:
- The reaction between <u>citric acid</u> and <u>sodium hydrogencarbonate</u>.
- <u>Thermal decomposition</u> — e.g. heating calcium carbonate causes it to decompose into calcium oxide (also called quicklime) and carbon dioxide:

Calcium carbonate $\longrightarrow$ $CaCO_{3(s)}$    (+ **HEAT**)    $\rightarrow$    $CO_{2(g)}$  +  $CaO_{(s)}$ $\longleftarrow$ Quicklime

2) Endothermic reactions also have everyday uses. For example:

> Endothermic reactions are used in some <u>sports injury packs</u> — the chemical reaction allows the pack to become <u>instantly cooler</u> without having to put it in the <u>freezer</u>.

# Exothermic and Endothermic Reactions

Sometimes it's <u>not enough</u> to just know if a reaction is <u>endothermic</u> or <u>exothermic</u>. You may also need to know <u>how much</u> energy is absorbed or released — you can do experiments to find this out. Fun, fun, fun...

## Energy Transfer can be Measured

1) You can measure the amount of <u>energy released</u> by a <u>chemical reaction</u> (in solution) by taking the <u>temperature of the reagents</u> (making sure they're the same), <u>mixing</u> them in a <u>polystyrene cup</u> and measuring the <u>temperature of the solution</u> at the <u>end</u> of the reaction (see diagram below).

2) The biggest <u>problem</u> with energy measurements is the amount of energy <u>lost to the surroundings</u>.

3) You can reduce it a bit by putting the polystyrene cup into a <u>beaker of cotton wool</u> to give <u>more insulation</u>, and putting a <u>lid</u> on the cup to reduce energy lost by <u>evaporation</u>.

4) This method works for <u>neutralisation reactions</u> or reactions between metals and acids, or carbonates and acids.

5) You can also use this method to investigate what effect different <u>variables</u> have on the amount of energy transferred — e.g. the <u>mass</u> or <u>concentration of the reactants</u> used.

Here's how you could test the effect of <u>acid concentration</u> on the energy released in a <u>neutralisation</u> reaction between hydrochloric acid (HCl) and sodium hydroxide (NaOH):

1) Put 25 cm³ of 0.25 mol/dm³ of <u>hydrochloric acid</u> and <u>sodium hydroxide</u> in separate beakers.

2) Place the beakers in a <u>water bath</u> set to 25 °C until they are both at the <u>same temperature</u> (25 °C).

3) Add the HCl followed by the NaOH to a <u>polystyrene cup</u> with a lid — as in the diagram.

4) Take the <u>temperature</u> of the mixture <u>every 30 seconds</u>, and record the highest temperature.

5) <u>Repeat</u> steps 1-4 using 0.5 mol/dm³ and then 1 mol/dm³ of hydrochloric acid.

## To get a reasonably accurate reading, insulate your reaction

The experiment on this page is an example of a neutralisation reaction, which is an <u>exothermic</u> reaction. Remember, in an exothermic reaction the particles <u>transfer</u> energy to their surroundings. This means that the <u>particles themselves</u> lose energy, but the <u>reaction mixture</u> gets warmer.

# Bond Energies

So you know that chemical reactions can take in or release energy — this page is about what <u>causes</u> these energy changes.  Hint — it's all to do with <u>making</u> and <u>breaking</u> chemical bonds.

## Energy Must Always be **Supplied** to **Break Bonds**

There's more on energy transfer on page 94.

1) During a chemical reaction, <u>old bonds are broken</u> and <u>new bonds are formed</u>.

2) Energy must be <u>supplied</u> to break <u>existing bonds</u> — so bond breaking is an <u>endothermic</u> process.

3) Energy is <u>released</u> when new bonds are <u>formed</u> — so bond formation is an <u>exothermic</u> process.

4) In <u>exothermic</u> reactions the energy <u>released</u> by forming bonds is <u>greater</u> than the energy used to <u>break</u> them.  In <u>endothermic</u> reactions the energy <u>used</u> to break bonds is <u>greater</u> than the energy released by forming them.

## **Reaction Profiles** Show **Energy Changes**

Reaction profiles are sometimes called energy level diagrams.

<u>Reaction profiles</u> are diagrams that show the <u>relative energies</u> of the reactants and products in a reaction, and how the energy <u>changes</u> over the course of the reaction.

1) This reaction profile shows an <u>exothermic reaction</u> — the products are at a <u>lower energy</u> than the reactants.  The difference in <u>height</u> represents the <u>overall energy change</u> in the reaction (the energy given out) per mole.

2) The <u>initial rise</u> in the line represents the energy needed to <u>break</u> the old bonds and start the reaction.  This is the <u>activation energy</u> ($E_a$).

3) The activation energy is the <u>minimum amount</u> of energy the reactants need to <u>collide with each other</u> and <u>react</u>.

4) The <u>greater</u> the activation energy, the <u>more</u> energy needed to <u>start</u> the reaction — this has to be <u>supplied</u>, e.g. by <u>heating</u> the reaction mixture.

There's more on activation energy and collision theory on pages 101-102.

5) This reaction profile shows an <u>endothermic reaction</u> because the products are at a <u>higher energy</u> than the reactants.

6) The <u>difference in height</u> represents the <u>overall energy change</u> during the reaction (the energy <u>taken in</u>) per mole.

# Bond Energies

You need to be able to <u>work out</u> the energy change for a particular reaction.
Here's a nice little <u>example</u>, complete with explanation, to get you started.

## Bond Energy **Calculations** Need to be **Practised**

1) <u>Every</u> chemical bond has a particular <u>bond energy</u> associated with it.
This <u>bond energy</u> varies slightly depending on what <u>compound</u> the bond occurs in.

2) You can use these <u>known bond energies</u> to calculate the <u>overall energy change</u> for a reaction.
The overall energy change is the <u>sum</u> of the energies <u>needed</u> to break bonds in the reactants
<u>minus</u> the energy <u>released</u> when the new bonds are formed in the products.

3) You need to <u>practise</u> a few of these, but the basic idea is really very simple...

**Using the bond energies given below, calculate the energy
change for the reaction between $H_2$ and $Cl_2$ forming HCl:**

$$H — H + Cl — Cl \rightarrow 2H — Cl$$
$$H_2 \quad + \quad Cl_2 \quad \rightarrow \quad 2HCl$$

The bond energies you need are:
- H—H:   +436 kJ/mol
- Cl—Cl:   +242 kJ/mol
- H—Cl:   +431 kJ/mol

1) Find the <u>energy required</u> to break the original bonds:

(1 × H–H)  +  (1 × Cl–Cl) = 436 kJ/mol + 242 kJ/mol  = 678 kJ/mol

2) Find the <u>energy released</u> by forming the new bonds.

2 × H–Cl  =  2 ×  431 kJ/mol = 862 kJ/mol

3) Find the <u>overall energy change</u> for the reaction using this equation:

Overall energy change = energy required to break bonds − energy released by forming bonds
= 678 kJ/mol − 862 kJ/mol = −184 kJ/mol

You <u>can't compare</u> the overall energy changes of reactions unless
you know the <u>numerical differences</u> in the bond energies.

Chlorine and bromine react with hydrogen in a similar way.  <u>Br–Br</u> bonds
are <u>weaker</u> than Cl–Cl bonds and <u>H–Br</u> bonds are <u>weaker</u> than H–Cl bonds.
So <u>less energy</u> is needed to <u>break</u> the bonds in the reaction with bromine,
but <u>less energy</u> is <u>released</u> when the new bonds form.  So unless you know
the <u>exact difference</u>, you can't say which reaction releases more energy.

## You need a balanced chemical equation for these calculations

**MATHS TIP** It's really helpful to <u>lay out</u> all of the information that you're given the way that is shown in the
worked example above.  That way you won't get all your bond energies mixed up and you'll be
able to clearly see what you have do in <u>each part</u> of the calculation.

# Warm-Up & Exam Questions

Funny diagrams, bond energy calculations, a practical — there's a lot to get your head around in just a few pages here. Here are some questions so that you can check how you're getting on.

## Warm-Up Questions

1) What is an exothermic reaction?
2) What is an endothermic reaction?
3) Is energy released when bonds are formed or when bonds are broken?
4) What is meant by the activation energy of a reaction?

## Exam Questions

**1** The diagrams in **Figure 1** represent the energy changes in four different chemical reactions.

**Figure 1**

Write the letter of **one** diagram, **A**, **B**, **C** or **D**, which illustrates an endothermic reaction.

*[1 mark]*

**PRACTICAL**

**2** A student places two beakers of ethanoic acid and dilute potassium hydroxide into a water bath until they are both 25 °C. He adds the ethanoic acid and then the potassium hydroxide to a polystyrene cup. After 1 minute the temperature of the mixture is 28.5 °C.

**2.1** Is this reaction endothermic or exothermic? Explain your answer.

*[2 marks]*

**2.2** The student put a lid on the polystyrene cup during the experiment. Suggest why this was done.

*[1 mark]*

**3** When methane burns in air it produces carbon dioxide and water, as shown in **Figure 2**.
The bond energies for each bond in the molecules involved are shown in **Figure 3**.

**Figure 3**

| | Bond energies (kJ/mol): |
|---|---|
| C – H | 414 |
| O = O | 494 |
| C = O | 800 |
| O – H | 459 |

**3.1** Which **two** types of bond are broken during the reaction shown in **Figure 2**?

*[1 mark]*

**3.2** Calculate the overall energy change for the reaction shown in **Figure 2**.

*[3 marks]*

# Revision Summary for Topic 5

Right, let's see how much you can remember. It's worth remembering that the bond energy stuff explains why chemical reactions give out or take in energy. If this isn't ringing any bells then go back and have another read through before having a go at the questions below.

- Try these questions and tick off each one when you get it right.
- When you've done all the questions under a heading and are completely happy with it, tick it off.

## Exothermic and Endothermic Reactions (p.94-95) ☑

1) In an exothermic reaction, is energy transferred to or from the surroundings? ☑

2) Name two different types of chemical reaction which are exothermic. ☑

3) Write down the symbol equation for the thermal decomposition of calcium carbonate. ☑

4) Give an everyday use of exothermic reactions. ☑

5) Give an everyday example of an endothermic reaction. ☑

6) A student mixed together a carbonate and an acid in a polystyrene cup and then measured the temperature change inside the cup during the reaction.
   a) The polystyrene cup was placed into a beaker filled with cotton wool during the experiment. Explain why this was done.
   b) The temperature goes up during the reaction. Is this reaction endothermic or exothermic? ☑

## Bond Energies (p.96-97) ☑

7) For the following sentences, use either endothermic or exothermic to fill in the blanks:
   a) Bond breaking is an _____ process.
   b) Bond forming is an _____ process.
   c) In an _____ reaction, the energy released by forming bonds is greater than the energy used to break them. ☑

8) Sketch an energy level diagram for an exothermic reaction. ☑

9) What is the alternative name for an energy level diagram? ☑

10) Which part of an energy level diagram shows the activation energy? ☑

11) Is the following statement true or false? In an endothermic reaction, the products of the reaction have more energy than the reactants. ☑

12) What three steps would you use to find the overall energy change in a reaction if you were given the known bond energies for the bonds present in the reactants and products? ☑

# Rates of Reaction

Rates of reaction are pretty <u>important</u>. In the <u>chemical industry</u>, the <u>faster</u> you make <u>chemicals</u>, the <u>faster</u> you make <u>money</u>.

## Reactions Can Go at All Sorts of **Different Rates**

1) The rate of a chemical reaction is how fast the <u>reactants</u> are <u>changed</u> into <u>products</u>.

2) One of the <u>slowest</u> is the rusting of iron (it's not slow enough though — what about my little Mini).

3) Other <u>slow</u> reactions include <u>chemical weathering</u> — like acid rain damage to limestone buildings.

4) An example of a <u>moderate speed</u> reaction would be the metal <u>magnesium</u> reacting with an <u>acid</u> to produce a gentle stream of bubbles.

5) <u>Burning</u> is a <u>fast</u> reaction, but <u>explosions</u> are even <u>faster</u> and release a lot of gas. Explosive reactions are all over in a <u>fraction of a second</u>.

## You Need to Understand **Graphs** for the **Rate of Reaction**

1) You can find the speed of a reaction by recording the amount of <u>product formed</u>, or the amount of <u>reactant used up</u> over <u>time</u> (see page 103).

2) The <u>steeper</u> the line on the graph, the <u>faster</u> the rate of reaction. <u>Over time</u> the line becomes <u>less steep</u> as the reactants are <u>used up</u>.

3) The <u>quickest reactions</u> have the <u>steepest</u> lines and become <u>flat</u> in the <u>least time</u>.

4) The plot below uses the amount of <u>product formed</u> over time to show how the <u>speed</u> of a particular reaction varies under <u>different conditions</u>.

For more on the conditions that affect the rate of reaction — see next page.

* Graph 1 represents the <u>original reaction</u>.
* Graphs 2 and 3 represent the reaction taking place <u>quicker</u>, but with the <u>same initial amounts</u> of reactants. The slopes of the graphs are <u>steeper</u> than for graph 1.
* Graphs 1, 2 and 3 all converge at the <u>same level</u>, showing that they all produce the <u>same amount</u> of product although they take <u>different times</u> to produce it.
* Graph 4 shows <u>more product</u> and a <u>faster reaction</u>. This can only happen if <u>more reactant(s)</u> are added at the start.

# Factors Affecting Rates of Reaction

I'd ask you to <u>guess</u> what these two pages are about, but the <u>title</u> pretty much says it all really. Read on...

## Particles Must **Collide** with **Enough Energy** in Order to **React**

1) Reaction rates are explained perfectly by <u>collision theory</u>. The <u>rate</u> of a chemical reaction depends on:

- The <u>collision frequency</u> of reacting particles (how <u>often</u> they collide). The <u>more</u> collisions there are the <u>faster</u> the reaction is. E.g. doubling the frequency of collisions doubles the rate.
- The energy <u>transferred</u> during a collision. Particles have to collide with <u>enough energy</u> for the collision to be successful.

*A successful collision is a collision that ends in the particles reacting to form products.*

2) You might remember from page 96 that the <u>minimum</u> amount of energy that particles need to react is called the <u>activation energy</u>. Particles need this much energy to <u>break the bonds</u> in the reactants and start the reaction.

3) Factors that <u>increase</u> the <u>number</u> of collisions (so that a <u>greater proportion</u> of reacting particles collide) or the amount of <u>energy</u> particles collide with will <u>increase</u> the <u>rate</u> of the reaction.

## The **Rate of Reaction** Depends on **Four Things**

1) <u>Temperature</u>.
2) The <u>concentration</u> of a solution or the <u>pressure</u> of gas.
3) <u>Surface area</u> — this changes depending on the size of the lumps of a solid.
4) The presence of a <u>catalyst</u>.

## **More Collisions** Increases the **Rate of Reaction**

All four methods of increasing the rate of a reaction can be explained in terms of increasing the <u>number</u> of <u>successful collisions</u> between the reacting particles:

### Increasing the **Temperature** Increases the Rate

1) When the temperature is <u>increased</u>, the particles all move <u>faster</u>.
2) If they're moving faster, they're going to collide more <u>frequently</u>.
3) Also the faster they move the <u>more energy</u> they have, so <u>more</u> of the <u>collisions</u> will have <u>enough energy</u> to make the reaction happen.

Cold

Hot

### Increasing the **Concentration** or **Pressure** Increases the Rate

1) If a solution is made more <u>concentrated</u>, it means there are <u>more particles</u> knocking about in the <u>same volume</u> of water (or other solvent).
2) Similarly, when the <u>pressure</u> of a gas is increased, it means that the <u>same number</u> of particles occupies a <u>smaller space</u>.
3) This makes <u>collisions</u> between the reactant particles <u>more frequent</u>.

Low concentration/ pressure | High concentration/ pressure

# Factors Affecting Rates of Reaction

## Increasing the **Surface Area** Increases the Rate

1) If one of the reactants is a <u>solid</u>, then breaking it up into <u>smaller pieces</u> will increase its <u>surface area to volume ratio</u>.

2) This means that for the <u>same volume</u> of the solid, the particles around it will have <u>more area</u> to work on — so there will be collisions <u>more frequently</u>.

Small surface area        Big surface area

## Using a **Catalyst** Increases the Rate

1) A catalyst is a substance that <u>speeds up</u> a reaction, <u>without</u> being <u>used up</u> in the reaction itself. This means it's <u>not</u> part of the overall reaction <u>equation</u>.

2) <u>Different</u> catalysts are needed for different reactions, but they all work by <u>decreasing</u> the <u>activation energy</u> needed for the reaction to occur. They do this by providing an <u>alternative reaction pathway</u> with a <u>lower</u> activation energy.

*This is a reaction profile. There's more on these on p.96.*

3) Enzymes are <u>biological catalysts</u> — they catalyse reactions in <u>living things</u>.

## It's easier to learn stuff when you know the reasons for it

Once you've learnt everything off these two pages, the rates of reaction stuff should start making a lot more sense to you. The concept's fairly simple — the <u>more often</u> particles bump into each other, and the <u>harder they hit</u> when they do, the <u>faster</u> the reaction happens.

# Measuring Rates of Reaction  PRACTICAL

All this talk about rates of reactions is fine and dandy, but it's no good if you can't <u>measure</u> it.

## You can **Calculate** the Rate of Reaction from **Experimental Results**

1) The rate of a reaction can be observed either by how quickly the <u>reactants are used up</u> or how quickly the <u>products are formed</u>:

$$\text{Rate of Reaction} = \frac{\text{Amount of reactant used or amount of product formed}}{\text{Time}}$$

2) When the product or reactant is a <u>gas</u> you usually measure the amount in <u>cm³</u>. If it's a <u>solid</u>, then you use <u>grams</u> (g).

3) Time is often measured in <u>seconds</u> (<u>s</u>).

4) This means that the units for rate may be in <u>cm³/s</u> or in <u>g/s</u>.

5) You can also measure the amount of product or reactant in <u>moles</u> — so the units of rate could also be <u>mol/s</u>.

6) There are <u>three different ways</u> of measuring the rate of a reaction:

*This is the mean rate of reaction. To find the rate of a reaction at a particular time, you'll need to plot a graph and find the gradient at that time (see page 107).*

## 1) **Precipitation** and **Colour Change**

1) You can record the <u>visual change</u> in a reaction if the initial solution is <u>transparent</u> and the product is a <u>precipitate</u> which <u>clouds</u> the solution (it becomes <u>opaque</u>).

2) You can observe a <u>mark</u> through the solution and measure how long it takes for it to <u>disappear</u> — the <u>faster</u> the mark disappears, the <u>quicker</u> the reaction.

3) If the reactants are <u>coloured</u> and the products are <u>colourless</u> (or vice versa), you can time how long it takes for the solution to <u>lose (or gain) its colour</u>.

4) The results are very <u>subjective</u> — <u>different people</u> might not agree over the <u>exact</u> point when the mark 'disappears' or the solution changes colour. Also, if you use this method, you can't plot a rate of reaction <u>graph</u> from the results.

*A posh way of saying that the cloudiness of a solution changes is to say that its 'turbidity' changes.*

 ## Make sure you use a method appropriate to your experiment
The method shown on this page only works if there's a <u>really obvious</u> change in the solution. If there's only a <u>small change</u> in colour, it <u>might not be possible</u> to observe and time the change.

# Measuring Rates of Reaction

## 2) Change in Mass (Usually Gas Given Off)

Putting cotton wool in the top of the flask lets the gas escape but stops the acid spitting out.

1) Measuring the speed of a reaction that produces a gas can be carried out using a mass balance.

2) As the gas is released, the mass disappearing is measured on the balance.

3) The quicker the reading on the balance drops, the faster the reaction.

4) If you take measurements at regular intervals, you can plot a rate of reaction graph and find the rate quite easily (see page 107 for more).

5) This is the most accurate of the three methods described because the mass balance is very accurate. But it has the disadvantage of releasing the gas straight into the room.

## 3) The Volume of Gas Given Off

1) This involves the use of a gas syringe to measure the volume of gas given off.

2) The more gas given off during a given time interval, the faster the reaction.

3) Gas syringes usually give volumes accurate to the nearest cm$^3$, so they're quite accurate. You can take measurements at regular intervals and plot a rate of reaction graph using this method too. You have to be quite careful though — if the reaction is too vigorous, you can easily blow the plunger out of the end of the syringe.

## Each of these three methods has pros and cons

The mass balance method is only accurate as long as the flask isn't too hot, otherwise the loss in mass that you see might be partly due to evaporation of liquid as well as being due to the loss of gas formed during the reaction. The first method (on the previous page) is subjective so it isn't very accurate, but if you're not producing a gas you can't use either of the other two.

# Rate Experiments

This page shows how you can use the method on the previous page in a <u>real investigation</u>.
Get your safety goggles on and let's go...

## Magnesium and HCl React to Produce H₂ Gas

1) Start by adding a set volume of <u>dilute hydrochloric acid</u> to a <u>conical flask</u>.
2) Now add some <u>magnesium ribbon</u> to the acid and quickly attach an empty <u>gas syringe</u> to the flask.
3) Start the <u>stopwatch</u>. Take <u>readings</u> of the <u>volume of gas</u> in the gas syringe at <u>regular intervals</u>.

You could also measure the gas released using a mass balance, as on the previous page.

4) Plot the results in a table.
5) Now you can plot a <u>graph</u> with <u>time</u> on the x-axis and <u>volume of gas produced</u> on the y-axis.

## You Can Investigate the Effect of Using Different Acid Concentrations

You can use the method above to investigate the <u>effect</u> of <u>acid concentration</u> on the rate of reaction:

1) You can repeat the experiment above with a number of different concentrations of acid. Variables such as the <u>amount</u> of magnesium ribbon and the <u>volume</u> of acid used should be <u>kept the same</u> each time — only change the acid's concentration. This is to make your experiment a <u>fair test</u> — see p.5.
2) If you plot all your results on the <u>same graph</u>, you can <u>compare</u> them to see how the concentration of acid affects the rate of reaction.
3) The three graphs show that a <u>higher concentration</u> of acid gives a <u>faster rate</u> of reaction.

The hypothesis for this experiment could be something like 'As the concentration of acid increases, the rate of reaction will increase.'

## Don't forget about any safety precautions you need to take

The graph above shows how to <u>compare</u> rates of reactions when using different concentrations of acid, but if you want to <u>calculate</u> a <u>numerical</u> value for the rate you need to use a calculation. Take a look at p.107 for how to find the rate of reaction from a graph.

# Rate Experiments

Here's how to use the method that you saw on page 103. It's a bit <u>less accurate</u> than using a mass balance, but you need to know how to do it in case you want to investigate a reaction that <u>doesn't produce a gas</u>.

## Sodium Thiosulfate and HCl Produce a Cloudy Precipitate

1) These two chemicals are both <u>clear solutions</u>.
   They react together to form a <u>yellow precipitate</u> of <u>sulfur</u>.

2) Start by adding a set volume of <u>dilute sodium thiosulfate</u> to a conical flask.

3) Place the flask on a piece of paper with a <u>black cross</u> drawn on it.

4) Add some <u>dilute HCl</u> to the flask and start the stopwatch.

5) Now watch the black cross <u>disappear</u> through the <u>cloudy sulfur</u> and <u>time</u> how long it takes to go.

*This reaction releases sulfur dioxide, so the experiment should be carried out in a well-ventilated place.*

*The hypothesis for this experiment could be something like 'As the concentration of acid increases, the solution will go cloudy more quickly.'*

## You Can Investigate How the Concentration of Acid Affects the Rate

1) The reaction can be <u>repeated</u> with solutions of either reactant at <u>different concentrations</u>. (Only change the concentration of <u>one reactant</u> at a time though.) The <u>depth</u> of the liquid must be kept the <u>same</u> each time.

2) These results show the effect of <u>increasing</u> the <u>concentration</u> of <u>HCl</u> on the rate of reaction, when added to an excess of sodium thiosulfate.

| Concentration of HCl (g/dm³) | 20 | 35 | 50 | 65 | 80 |
|---|---|---|---|---|---|
| Time taken for mark to disappear (s) | 193 | 184 | 178 | 171 | 164 |

3) The <u>higher</u> the concentration, the <u>quicker</u> the reaction and therefore the <u>less time</u> it takes for the mark to disappear.

4) One sad thing about this reaction is that it <u>doesn't</u> give a set of <u>graphs</u>. Well I think it's sad. All you get is a set of <u>readings</u> of how long it took till the mark disappeared for each concentration. Boring.

*Although you could draw a graph of concentration against 1/time which will give you an approximate rate.*

---

## Make sure you can clearly see the cross through the flask at the start

Makes sure you learn <u>both</u> the methods on these two pages for investigating rate, but don't forget that other methods (e.g. the one using a balance that you saw earlier in the topic) can also be used. It's not just the effect of <u>concentration</u> you can investigate with these experiments, either — you can also use them to see how other factors (such as <u>temperature</u>, <u>surface area</u> or the <u>presence of a catalyst</u>) affect rate.

# Finding Reaction Rates from Graphs

You might remember a bit about how to <u>interpret</u> graphs on reaction rate from page 100 — well this page shows you how to use them to <u>calculate</u> rates.

## You can Calculate the **Mean Reaction Rate** from a **Graph**

1) Remember, a rate of reaction graph shows the amount of <u>product formed</u> or amount of <u>reactant used up</u> on the <u>y-axis</u> and <u>time</u> on the x-axis.

2) So to find the <u>mean rate</u> for the <u>whole reaction</u>, you just work out the <u>overall change</u> in the y-value and then <u>divide this</u> by the <u>total time taken</u> for the reaction.

3) You can also use the graph to find the <u>mean rate</u> of reaction between <u>any two points</u> in time:

 **EXAMPLE:**

**The graph shows the volume of gas released by a reaction, measured at regular intervals. Find the mean rate of reaction between 20 s and 40 s.**

Mean rate of reaction = change in y ÷ change in x
$$= (19 \text{ cm}^3 - 15 \text{ cm}^3) \div 20 \text{ s}$$
$$= 0.2 \text{ cm}^3/\text{s}$$

If you're asked to find the mean rate of reaction for the whole reaction, remember that the reaction finishes as soon as the line on the graph goes flat.

## Draw a **Tangent** to Find the **Reaction Rate** at a **Particular Point**

If you want to find the <u>rate</u> of the reaction at a particular point in time, you need to find the <u>gradient</u> (slope) of the curve at that point. The easiest way to do this is to draw a <u>tangent</u> to the curve — a straight line that touches the curve at one point and doesn't cross it. You then work out the <u>gradient of the tangent</u>. It's simpler than it sounds, honest...

**EXAMPLE:**

**The graph below shows the mass of reactant used up measured at regular intervals during a chemical reaction. What is the rate of reaction at 3 minutes?**

1) Position a <u>ruler</u> on the graph at the point where you want to know the rate — here it's <u>3 minutes</u>.

2) Adjust the ruler until the <u>space</u> between the ruler and the curve is <u>equal</u> on <u>both sides</u> of the point.

3) Draw a line along the ruler to make the <u>tangent</u>. Extend the line <u>right across</u> the graph.

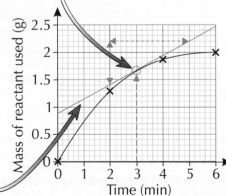

4) Pick <u>two points</u> on the line that are easy to read. Use them to calculate the <u>gradient</u> of the tangent in order to find the <u>rate</u>:

gradient = change in y ÷ change in x
$$= (2.2 - 1.4) \div (5.0 - 2.0)$$
$$= 0.8 \div 3.0$$
$$= 0.27$$

So, the rate of reaction at 3 minutes was 0.27 g/min.

# PRACTICAL Warm-Up & Exam Questions

It's easy to think that you've understood something when you've just read through it. These questions should test whether you really understand the previous chunk of pages, and get you set for the next bit.

## Warm-Up Questions

1) Give an example of a reaction that happens very slowly, and one that is very fast.
2) According to collision theory, what must happen in order for two particles to react?
3) Why does increasing the concentration of solutions increase the rate of a reaction?
4) What units of rate would be used for a reaction where the change in mass of a reaction vessel (measured in grams) has been recorded over time (measured in seconds)?
5) Describe how you could measure the rate of a precipitation reaction.

## Exam Questions

1 **Figure 1** shows one method of measuring the rate of a reaction which produces a gas.

**Figure 1**

conical flask

1.1 What piece of apparatus necessary for measuring the rate of this reaction, is missing from **Figure 1**?

*[1 mark]*

1.2 Name of the piece of apparatus in **Figure 1** labelled **X**.

*[1 mark]*

1.3 Describe **one** other method of measuring the rate of a reaction which produces a gas.

*[2 marks]*

2 Set volumes of sodium thiosulfate and hydrochloric acid were reacted at different temperatures. The time taken for a black cross to be obscured by the sulfur precipitate was measured at each temperature. The results are shown in **Table 1**.

**Table 1**

2.1 Give **two** variables that should be kept constant in this experiment.

*[2 marks]*

| Temperature (°C) | Time (s) |
|---|---|
| 55 | 6 |
| 36 | 11 |
| 24 | 17 |
| 16 | 27 |
| 9 | 40 |
| 5 | 51 |

2.2 Plot the results on a graph (with time on the *x*-axis) and draw a line of best fit.

*[4 marks]*

2.3 Describe the relationship illustrated by your graph.

*[1 mark]*

2.4 Describe how the results would change if the experiment was repeated with a **lower** concentration of sodium thiosulfate.

*[1 mark]*

2.5 Explain how using a lower reactant concentration affects the rate of a reaction.

*[3 marks]*

2.6 Suggest how you could assess if the results of the experiment are repeatable.

*[2 marks]*

# Exam Questions

**3**    A teacher demonstrated an experiment to investigate the effect of temperature on the rate of a reaction. The teacher added dilute hydrochloric acid at 20 °C to marble chips and measured the volume of gas produced at regular time intervals. The teacher then repeated the experiment at 30 °C using the same mass of marble chips of the same size. The results are shown in **Figure 2**.

**Figure 2**

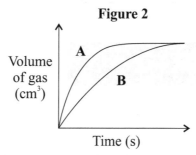

**3.1**    On **Figure 2**, which curve, **A** or **B**, shows the result of the experiment at 30 °C?

*[1 mark]*

**3.2**    Sketch the curve you would expect if you repeated the experiment at 25 °C onto **Figure 2**. Label it **C**.

*[1 mark]*

**3.3**    The teacher made sure that the same volume and concentration of acid was used in each repeat. Explain why these variables needed to be controlled.

*[1 mark]*

**3.4**    Does **Figure 2** suggest that the teacher successfully controlled these variables? Explain your answer.

*[1 mark]*

**3.5**    Which of the following methods could also be used to measure the rate of this reaction?
Tick **one** box.

Measuring how quickly the reaction loses mass. ☐

Timing how long the reaction takes to go cloudy. ☐

Timing how long the reaction takes to start. ☐

*[1 mark]*

**4**    Calcium carbonate powder was added to a conical flask containing dilute HCl. $CO_2$ was produced and collected in a gas syringe. The volume of gas released was recorded at 10 second intervals in **Table 2**:

**Table 2**

| Time (s) | 0 | 10 | 20 | 30 | 40 | 50 | 60 |
|---|---|---|---|---|---|---|---|
| Volume of $CO_2$ (cm³) | 0 | 24 | 32 | 36 | 38 | 39 | 40 |

**4.1**    Calculate the mean rate of reaction between 0 and 60 seconds.

*[2 marks]*

**4.2**    Plot these results on a graph and draw a line of best fit.

*[4 marks]*

**4.3**    Find the rate of the reaction 25 seconds after starting the experiment.

*[4 marks]*

**5\***    Hydrogen gas and ethene gas react to form ethane.
Nickel can be used as a catalyst for this reaction.

Using your knowledge of collision theory, explain how the rate of this reaction can be increased.

*[6 marks]*

# Reversible Reactions

Some reactions can go <u>backwards</u>.  Honestly, that's all you need...

## Reversible Reactions Will Reach Equilibrium

This equation shows a <u>reversible reaction</u> — the <u>products</u> (C and D)
can react to form the <u>reactants</u> (A and B) again:

$$A + B \rightleftharpoons C + D$$

The '$\rightleftharpoons$' shows the reaction
goes both ways.

1) As the <u>reactants</u> react, their concentrations <u>fall</u> — so the <u>forward reaction</u>
   will <u>slow down</u> (see page 101).  But as more and more <u>products</u> are made
   and their concentrations <u>rise</u>, the <u>backward reaction</u> will <u>speed up</u>.

2) After a while the forward reaction will be going at <u>exactly the
   same rate</u> as the backward one — the system is at <u>equilibrium</u>.

3) At equilibrium, <u>both</u> reactions are still happening, but there's <u>no overall effect</u>
   (it's a dynamic equilibrium).  This means the <u>concentrations</u> of reactants and
   products have reached a balance and <u>won't change</u>.

4) Equilibrium is only reached if the reversible reaction takes place
   in a 'closed system'.  A <u>closed system</u> just means that <u>none</u> of the
   reactants or products can <u>escape</u> and nothing else can get <u>in</u>.

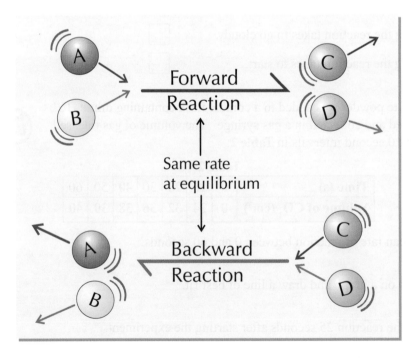

## Dynamic equilibrium — lots of activity, but not to any great effect

The idea of <u>dynamic equilibrium</u> is something that you need to get to grips with, as things will get <u>more</u>
<u>complicated</u> on the next couple of pages.  Have <u>another read</u> and make sure you've got the basics sorted.

# Reversible Reactions

In a reversible reaction, both the forward and the reverse reactions are happening <u>at the same time</u>. Certain conditions can be <u>more favourable</u> to one reaction than the other, making it happen faster.

## The **Position of Equilibrium** Can be on the **Right** or the **Left**

1) When a reaction's at equilibrium it <u>doesn't</u> mean the amounts of reactants and products are <u>equal</u>.
2) If the equilibrium <u>lies to the right</u>, the concentration of <u>products</u> is <u>greater</u> than that of the reactants.
3) If the equilibrium <u>lies to the left</u>, the concentration of <u>reactants</u> is <u>greater</u> than that of the products.
4) The <u>position of equilibrium</u> depends on the following <u>conditions</u> (as well as the reaction itself):

1) the <u>temperature</u>,
2) the <u>pressure</u> (this only affects equilibria involving gases),
3) the <u>concentration</u> of the reactants and products.

E.g. ammonium chloride $\rightleftharpoons$ ammonia + hydrogen chloride
<u>Heating</u> this reaction moves the equilibrium to the <u>right</u> (more ammonia and hydrogen chloride) and <u>cooling</u> it moves it to the <u>left</u> (more ammonium chloride).

*The next page tells you why these things affect equilibrium position.*

## Reversible Reactions Can Be **Endothermic** and **Exothermic**

1) In reversible reactions, if the reaction is <u>endothermic</u> in one direction, it will be <u>exothermic</u> in the other.
2) The energy transferred <u>from</u> the surroundings by the endothermic reaction is <u>equal to</u> the energy transferred <u>to</u> the surroundings during the exothermic reaction.
3) A good example is the <u>thermal decomposition</u> of hydrated copper sulfate:

*See page 94 for more on endothermic and exothermic reactions.*

endothermic

**hydrated copper sulfate** $\rightleftharpoons$ **anhydrous copper sulfate + water**

exothermic

'Anhydrous' just means 'without water', and 'hydrated' means 'with water'.

If you <u>heat blue hydrated</u> copper(II) sulfate crystals, it drives the water off and leaves <u>white anhydrous</u> copper(II) sulfate powder. This is <u>endothermic</u>.

If you then <u>add</u> a couple of drops of <u>water</u> to the <u>white powder</u> you get the <u>blue crystals</u> back again. This is <u>exothermic</u>.

---

REVISION TIP

## More of the products = equilibrium lies to the right

This whole energy transfer thing is a fairly simple idea — don't be put off by the long words. Remember, "<u>exo-</u>" = <u>external</u>, "<u>-thermic</u>" = <u>heat</u>, so an exothermic reaction is one that <u>gives out</u> heat. And "<u>endo-</u>" = erm... the other one. OK, there's no easy way to remember that one. Tough.

# Le Chatelier's Principle

Reversible reactions don't like being messed around — so if you change something,
the system will <u>respond</u> to undo the change.

## Reversible Reactions Try to Counteract Changes...

1) <u>Le Chatelier's Principle</u> is the idea that if you change the <u>conditions</u> of a
reversible reaction at equilibrium, the system will try to <u>counteract</u> that change.

2) It can be used to <u>predict</u> the effect of any changes you make to a reaction system.

## ...Such as Changes to the Temperature...

1) All reactions are <u>exothermic</u> in one direction and <u>endothermic</u> in the other (see previous page).

2) If you <u>decrease</u> the temperature, the equilibrium will move
in the <u>exothermic direction</u> to produce more heat.
This means you'll get <u>more products</u> for the <u>exothermic</u>
reaction and fewer products for the endothermic reaction.

3) If you <u>raise</u> the temperature, the equilibrium will move
in the <u>endothermic direction</u> to try and decrease it.
You'll now get <u>more products</u> for the <u>endothermic</u> reaction
and fewer products for the exothermic reaction.

> $N_2 + 3H_2 \rightleftharpoons 2NH_3$
>
> Here the forward reaction is
> exothermic — a decrease in
> temperature moves equilibrium
> to the right (more $NH_3$).

## ...Pressure...

1) Changing the pressure only affects an equilibrium involving <u>gases</u>.

2) If you <u>increase</u> the pressure, the equilibrium tries to <u>reduce</u> it —
it moves in the direction where there are <u>fewer</u> molecules of gas.

3) If you <u>decrease</u> the pressure, the equilibrium tries to <u>increase</u> it —
it moves in the direction where there are <u>more</u> molecules of gas.

4) You can use the <u>balanced symbol equation</u> for a reaction
to see which side has more molecules of gas.

> $N_2 + 3H_2 \rightleftharpoons 2NH_3$
>
> There are 4 moles on the left
> (1 of $N_2$ and 3 of $H_2$) but only 2
> on the right. So, if you increase
> the pressure, the equilibrium
> shifts to the right (more $NH_3$).

## ...or Concentration

1) If you change the concentration of <u>either</u> the reactants or the
products, the system will <u>no longer</u> be at equilibrium.

2) So the system responds to bring itself <u>back</u> to equilibrium again.

3) If you increase the concentration of the <u>reactants</u> the system
tries to decrease it by making more <u>products</u>.

4) If you decrease the concentration of <u>products</u> the system
tries to increase it again by reducing the amount of <u>reactants</u>.

> $N_2 + 3H_2 \rightleftharpoons 2NH_3$
>
> If more $N_2$ or $H_2$ is added,
> the forward reaction increases
> to produce more $NH_3$.

---

## So, you do one thing, and the reaction does the other...

The best way to get your head around all this is to <u>practise it</u>. So find a reversible reaction,
and then think about how <u>changing each condition</u> will affect the <u>position of equilibrium</u>.

# Warm-Up & Exam Questions

Not long now 'til this section's over, but first there are some questions for you to tackle.

## Warm-Up Questions

1) What can you say about forward and backward reaction rates at equilibrium?
2) For a reversible reaction, what is the effect on equilibrium of removing some of the reactants from the reaction mixture?
3) For the reaction, $N_{2(g)} + O_{2(g)} \rightleftharpoons 2NO_{(g)}$, what would be the effect on the equilibrium of changing the gas pressure?

## Exam Questions

**1** In the reaction below, substances A and B react to form substances C and D.

$$2A + B \rightleftharpoons 2C + D$$

**1.1** What can you deduce about this reaction from the symbol $\rightleftharpoons$ ?

*[1 mark]*

**1.2** What is meant by the term **dynamic equilibrium**?

*[1 mark]*

**2** This question is about how pressure affects the position of equilibrium.

Reaction 1: $N_2O_{4(g)} \rightleftharpoons 2NO_{2(g)}$

Reaction 2: $ClNO_{2(g)} + NO_{(g)} \rightleftharpoons NO_{2(g)} + ClNO_{(g)}$

**2.1** For Reaction 1, explain the effect of an **increase** in pressure on the amount of products at equilibrium.

*[2 marks]*

**2.2** For Reaction 2, explain the effect of a **decrease** in pressure on the amount of products at equilibrium.

*[2 marks]*

**3** When calcium carbonate is heated to a high temperature in a closed system, an equilibrium is reached:

$$CaCO_{3(s)} \rightleftharpoons CaO_{(s)} + CO_{2(g)}$$

The forward reaction is endothermic.

**3.1** Does the reverse reaction take in or give out energy? Explain your answer.

*[2 marks]*

**3.2** Explain why changing the temperature of a reversible reaction always affects the position of the equilibrium.

*[2 marks]*

**3.3** For the reaction shown above, describe what would happen to the equilibrium position if the temperature was raised.

*[1 mark]*

# Revision Summary for Topic 6

We'll you've almost made it — you're just one more page away from a lovely cup of tea and a biscuit...
• Try these questions and <u>tick off each one</u> when you <u>get it right</u>.
• When you've done <u>all the questions</u> under a heading and are <u>completely happy</u> with it, tick it off.

## Rates of Reaction and Factors Affecting Them (p.100-102) ☑

1) On a rate of reaction graph, what does a steep line show?
2) On a rate of reaction graph, what does a flat line show?
3) What two factors relating to the collisions between particles influence the rate of a reaction?
4) What are the four factors that affect the rate of a reaction?
5) Why does increasing the temperature of a reaction mixture increase the rate of a reaction?
6) What is a catalyst?
7) How does a catalyst increase the rate of a reaction?

## Measuring and Calculating Rates of Reaction (p.103-107) ☑

8) State the equation that could be used to calculate the mean rate of a reaction.
9) Give three possible units for the rate of a chemical reaction.
10) Explain why measuring a mass change during a reaction is usually an accurate method of measuring rate.
11) Describe how you could investigate the effect of increasing HCl concentration on the rate of reaction between HCl and Mg.
12) Describe how you could use a graph to find the mean rate of a reaction between two points in time.
13) What is a tangent?
14) How would you use a tangent to find the gradient of a curve at a particular point?

## Reversible Reactions and Le Chatelier's Principle (p.110-112) ☑

15) Which one of the following statements is true?
   a) In a reaction at equilibrium, there is the same amount of products as reactants.
   b) If the forward reaction in a reversible reaction is exothermic, then the reverse reaction is endothermic.
   c) If the equilibrium of a system lies to the right, then the concentration of products is less than the concentration of reactants.
16) What effect will decreasing the temperature have on a reversible reaction in which the forward reaction is exothermic?
17) In a reversible reaction between gases, how will the equilibrium position change if the pressure is increased?
18) In a reversible reaction, what effect will decreasing the concentration of the products for the forward reaction have on the equilibrium position?

# Hydrocarbons

Organic chemistry is about compounds that contain <u>carbon</u>. <u>Hydrocarbons</u> are the simplest organic compounds. As you're about to discover, their <u>properties</u> are affected by their <u>structure</u>.

## Hydrocarbons Only Contain **Hydrogen** and **Carbon** Atoms

1) A hydrocarbon is any compound that is formed from <u>carbon and hydrogen atoms only</u>.

2) So $C_{10}H_{22}$ (decane, an alkane) is a hydrocarbon, but $CH_3COOC_3H_7$ (an ester) is <u>not</u> — it contains oxygen.

## Alkanes Have All C–C **Single** Bonds

1) <u>Alkanes</u> are the simplest type of hydrocarbon you can get. Their <u>general formula</u> is:

$$C_nH_{2n+2}$$

2) The alkanes are a <u>homologous series</u> — a group of organic compounds that react in a similar way.

3) Alkanes are <u>saturated compounds</u> — each carbon atom forms four single covalent bonds.

4) The first four alkanes are <u>methane</u>, <u>ethane</u>, <u>propane</u> and <u>butane</u>.

*A drawing showing all the atoms and bonds in a molecule is called a displayed formula.*

**Methane**
Formula: $CH_4$

**Ethane**
Formula: $C_2H_6$

**Propane**
Formula: $C_3H_8$

**Butane**
Formula: $C_4H_{10}$

---

## Hydrocarbons only contain hydrogen and carbon

To help remember the names of the <u>first four alkanes</u> just remember: <u>M</u>ice <u>E</u>at <u>P</u>eanut <u>B</u>utter. Practise drawing the structures and get to grips with their formulas using the general formula.

# Hydrocarbons

## Hydrocarbon **Properties Change** as the Chain Gets **Longer**

As the <u>length</u> of the carbon chain changes, the <u>properties</u> of the hydrocarbon change:

1) The <u>shorter</u> the carbon chain, the <u>more runny</u> the hydrocarbon is
   — that is, the <u>less viscous</u> (gloopy) it is.

2) The <u>shorter</u> the carbon chain, the <u>more volatile</u> the hydrocarbon is. "More volatile" means
   it turns into a gas at a <u>lower temperature</u>. So, the shorter the carbon chain, the <u>lower</u> the
   <u>temperature</u> at which that hydrocarbon <u>vaporises</u> or <u>condenses</u> — and the <u>lower</u> its <u>boiling point</u>.

3) Also, the <u>shorter</u> the carbon chain, the more <u>flammable</u> (easier to ignite) the hydrocarbon is.

The <u>properties</u> of hydrocarbons affect how they're used for fuels.
E.g. <u>short chain</u> hydrocarbons with <u>lower</u> boiling points are used
as 'bottled gases' — stored <u>under pressure</u> as <u>liquids</u> in bottles.

## Complete Combustion Occurs When There's Plenty of Oxygen

1) The <u>complete combustion</u> of any hydrocarbon in oxygen releases lots of energy.
   The only waste products are <u>carbon dioxide</u> and <u>water</u> vapour.

$$\text{hydrocarbon} + \text{oxygen} \rightarrow \text{carbon dioxide} + \text{water} \quad (+ \text{ energy})$$

2) During combustion, both carbon and hydrogen from the hydrocarbon are <u>oxidised</u>.
   Oxidation can be defined as the gain of oxygen.

3) Hydrocarbons are used as <u>fuels</u> due to the <u>amount of energy</u> released when they combust completely.

4) You need to be able to give a <u>balanced symbol equation</u> for the <u>complete combustion</u> of a simple
   hydrocarbon fuel when you're given its <u>molecular formula</u>. It's pretty easy — here's an example:

 **Write a balanced equation for the complete combustion of methane ($CH_4$).**

1) On the <u>left hand side</u>, there's <u>one</u> carbon atom, so
   only <u>one</u> molecule of $CO_2$ is needed to balance this.

   $CH_4 + ?O_2 \rightarrow CO_2 + ?H_2O$

2) On the <u>left hand side</u>, there are <u>four</u> hydrogen atoms,
   so <u>two</u> water molecules are needed to balance them.

   $CH_4 + ?O_2 \rightarrow CO_2 + 2H_2O$

3) There are <u>four</u> oxygen atoms on the <u>right hand side</u> of the equation.
   <u>Two</u> oxygen molecules are needed on the left to balance them.

   $CH_4 + 2O_2 \rightarrow CO_2 + 2H_2O$

## Alkanes are useful fuels as they release energy when burnt

So <u>shorter</u> hydrocarbons are less viscous, more volatile and easier to ignite than <u>longer</u> hydrocarbons.

# Fractional Distillation

Crude oil can be used to make loads of useful things, such as fuels. But you can't just put crude oil in your car. First, the different hydrocarbons have to be separated. That's where fractional distillation comes in.

## Crude Oil is Made Over a Long Period of Time

1) Crude oil is a fossil fuel. It's formed from the remains of plants and animals, mainly plankton, that died millions of years ago and were buried in mud. Over millions of years, with high temperature and pressure, the remains turn to crude oil, which can be drilled up from the rocks where it's found.

2) Fossil fuels like coal, oil and gas are called non-renewable fuels as they take so long to make that they're being used up much faster than they're being formed. They're finite resources (see p.137) — one day they'll run out.

## Fractional Distillation is Used to Separate Hydrocarbon Fractions

1) Crude oil is a mixture of lots of different hydrocarbons, most of which are alkanes. Hydrocarbons are molecules containing only hydrogen and carbon.

2) The different compounds in crude oil are separated by fractional distillation.

APPROXIMATE NUMBER OF CARBONS IN THE HYDROCARBONS IN THAT FRACTION

~3

~8

~15

~20

~40

Crude Oil

COOL

LPG (Liquefied Petroleum Gas)

LPG contains mostly propane and butane.

Petrol

Kerosene

Diesel Oil

Heavy fuel oil

Very Hot

This can be heating oil, fuel oil or lubricating oil.

Here's how it works:

- The oil is heated until most of it has turned into gas. The gases enter a fractionating column (and the liquid bit is drained off).

- In the column there's a temperature gradient (it's hot at the bottom and gets cooler as you go up).

- The longer hydrocarbons have high boiling points. They condense back into liquids and drain out of the column early on, when they're near the bottom. The shorter hydrocarbons have lower boiling points. They condense and drain out much later on, near to the top of the column where it's cooler.

- You end up with the crude oil mixture separated out into different fractions. Each fraction contains a mixture of hydrocarbons that all contain a similar number of carbon atoms, so have similar boiling points.

# Uses and Cracking of Crude Oil

Crude oil has fuelled <u>modern civilisation</u> — it would be a very different world if we hadn't discovered oil.

## Crude Oil has Various Uses Important in Modern Life

1) <u>Oil</u> provides the <u>fuel</u> for most modern <u>transport</u> — cars, trains, planes, the lot. Diesel oil, kerosene, heavy fuel oil and LPG (liquid petroleum gas) all come from crude oil.

2) The <u>petrochemical industry</u> uses some of the hydrocarbons from crude oil as a <u>feedstock</u> to make <u>new compounds</u> for use in things like <u>polymers</u>, <u>solvents</u>, <u>lubricants</u>, and <u>detergents</u>.

3) All the products you get from crude oil are examples of <u>organic compounds</u> (compounds containing carbon atoms). The reason you get such a large <u>variety</u> of products is because carbon atoms can bond together to form different groups called <u>homologous series</u>. These groups contain <u>similar compounds</u> with many properties in common.

## Cracking Means Splitting Up Long-Chain Hydrocarbons

1) <u>Short-chain hydrocarbons</u> are flammable so make good fuels and are in high demand. However, <u>long-chain hydrocarbons</u> form <u>thick gloopy liquids</u> like <u>tar</u> which aren't all that useful.

2) As a result of this a lot of the longer alkane molecules produced from <u>fractional distillation</u> are <u>turned</u> into <u>smaller, more useful</u> ones by a process called <u>cracking</u>.

3) As well as alkanes, cracking also produces another type of hydrocarbon called <u>alkenes</u>. Alkenes are used as a <u>starting material</u> when making lots of other compounds and can be used to make polymers.

<u>Bromine water</u> can be used to test for alkenes.
1) When orange <u>bromine water</u> is added to an <u>alkane</u>, no reaction will happen and it'll stay <u>bright orange</u>.
2) If bromine water is added to an <u>alkene</u> a reaction occurs because alkenes are <u>more reactive</u> than alkanes. This results in a <u>colourless</u> compound being produced and the bromine water being <u>decolourised</u>.

bromine water + an alkene    solution goes colourless

4) Some of the products of cracking are useful as <u>fuels</u>, e.g. petrol for cars and paraffin for jet fuel.

## There are Different Methods of Cracking

1) <u>Cracking</u> is a <u>thermal decomposition</u> reaction — <u>breaking molecules down</u> by <u>heating</u> them.
2) The first step is to <u>heat</u> long-chain hydrocarbons to <u>vaporise</u> them (turn them into a gas).
3) Then the <u>vapour</u> can be passed over a <u>hot</u> powdered aluminium oxide <u>catalyst</u>.
4) The <u>long-chain</u> molecules <u>split apart</u> on the <u>surface</u> of the specks of catalyst — this is <u>catalytic cracking</u>.
5) You can also crack hydrocarbons if you vaporise them, mix them with <u>steam</u> and then <u>heat</u> them to a very high temperature. This is known as <u>steam cracking</u>.

*Make sure that, when writing equations for cracking, there are the <u>same number</u> of carbon and hydrogen atoms on <u>both sides</u> of the equation.*

# Warm-Up & Exam Questions

Hydrocarbons contain only hydrogen and carbon atoms. This page contains only Warm-Up and Exam Questions. Time to get thinking.

## Warm-Up Questions

1) Name the first four alkanes.
2) What kind of bonds are present in alkanes?
3) Why are alkanes often used as fuels?
4) Suggest a use of crude oil fractions that modern society depends on.
5) What sort of hydrocarbon molecules are cracked?

## Exam Questions

**1**  Which alkane is shown below? *(Grade 4-6)*
Tick **one** box.

$$H-\underset{\underset{H}{|}}{\overset{\overset{H}{|}}{C}}-\underset{\underset{H}{|}}{\overset{\overset{H}{|}}{C}}-H$$

butane ☐     propane ☐     ethane ☐     methane ☐

*[1 mark]*

**2**  Alkanes are a homologous series of hydrocarbons made up of chains *(Grade 4-6)* of carbon atoms surrounded by hydrogen atoms.

Pentane is an alkane with the formula $C_5H_{12}$.

**2.1**  State the name of the alkane that comes before pentane in the homologous series.

*[1 mark]*

**2.2**  State the formula of the alkane that comes before pentane in the homologous series.

*[1 mark]*

**2.3**  Suggest **two** materials produced from hydrocarbons by the petrochemical industry.

*[2 marks]*

**3**  Draw **one** line from each property of hydrocarbons to its trend with changing molecular size. *(Grade 4-6)*

| **Property** | **Trend** |
|---|---|
| Flammability | Increases as the molecules get bigger |
| Viscosity | |
| Boiling point | Decreases as the molecules get bigger |

*[3 marks]*

# Exam Questions

4    Crude oil can be separated into a number of different compounds in a
     fractional distillation column. **Figure 1** shows a fractional distillation column.

**Figure 1**

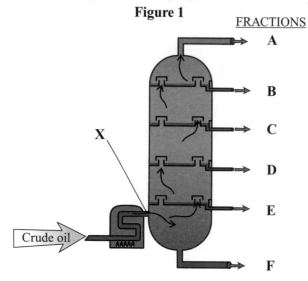

FRACTIONS

4.1    Which letter, **A-F**, represents the fraction with the longest hydrocarbon molecules?

*[1 mark]*

4.2    Which letter, **A-F**, represents the fraction with the lowest boiling point?

*[1 mark]*

4.3    Gaseous crude oil enters near the bottom of the fractional distillation column (point **X** in **Figure 1**).
       Explain why different fractions exit the column at different points and how this relates to their structure.

*[3 marks]*

5    Alkanes burn in excess oxygen by complete combustion.

5.1    What two products are made by the complete combustion of an alkane?

*[2 marks]*

5.2    Complete the equation below for the complete combustion of propane ($C_3H_8$):

$$C_3H_8 \; + \; ......O_2 \; \rightarrow \; .......... \; + \; ..........$$

*[2 marks]*

5.3    Carbon and hydrogen atoms gain oxygen during the combustion of hydrocarbons.
       What type of reaction is this?

*[1 mark]*

6    Cracking is a process used to break longer chain molecules in crude oil down to shorter ones.

6.1    Why is cracking an important process in the petrochemical industry?

*[1 mark]*

6.2    Octane ($C_8H_{18}$) can be cracked to form two products, ethane and propene ($C_3H_6$).
       Complete the equation below for this reaction:

$$C_8H_{18} \; \rightarrow \; .............. \; + \; ......C_3H_6$$

*[2 marks]*

6.3    Describe the **two** methods used by the petrochemical industry for cracking hydrocarbons.

*[4 marks]*

# Revision Summary for Topic 7

That wraps up <u>Topic 7</u> — time to put yourself to the test and find out <u>how much you really know</u>.

- Try these questions and <u>tick off each one</u> when you <u>get it right</u>.
- When you've done <u>all the questions</u> under a heading and are <u>completely happy</u> with it, tick it off.

## Hydrocarbons (p.115-116) ☑

1) What two elements do hydrocarbons contain?
2) What is the general formula for alkanes?
3) What type of bond exists between atoms in an alkane?
4) Name the alkane that contains three carbon atoms.
5) Draw the displayed formula of butane.
6) Give one factor which affects the boiling point of hydrocarbons.
7) What is the general word equation for the complete combustion of a hydrocarbon?
8) Write a balanced symbol equation for the complete combustion of methane ($CH_4$).

## Fractional Distillation (p.117) ☑

9) How is crude oil formed?
10) Crude oil is described as a non-renewable resource. What does this mean?
11) Where are the shortest carbon chains found in the fractional distillation column?
12) Which is the hottest part of a fractional distillation column?
13) What is meant by the term 'fraction'?

## Uses and Cracking of Crude Oil (p.118) ☑

14) What happens to long-chain hydrocarbons when they undergo cracking?
15) What is used to test for alkenes?
16) Cracking is a thermal decomposition reaction. Explain what this means.
17) Name two methods of cracking.
18) Write an equation using displayed formulas that shows the cracking of decane into octane and ethene.
19) Give a product of cracking that is used for making plastics.

# Purity and Formulations

Substances are often not 100% pure — they might have other stuff that you can't see mixed in with them. The purity of a substance might need to be checked, before, say, a drug is made from it.

## Purity is Defined Differently in Chemistry to Everyday

1) Usually when you refer to a substance as being pure you mean that nothing has been added to it, so it's in its natural state. For example, pure milk or beeswax.

2) In chemistry, a pure substance is something that only contains one compound or element throughout — not mixed with anything else.

## The Boiling or Melting Point Tells You How Pure a Substance Is

1) A chemically pure substance will melt or boil at a specific temperature.

2) You can test the purity of a sample by measuring its melting or boiling point and comparing it with the melting or boiling point of the pure substance (which you can find in a data book).

3) The closer your measured value is to the actual melting or boiling point, the purer your sample is.

4) Impurities in your sample will lower the melting point and increase the melting range of your substance.

5) Impurities in your sample will also increase the boiling point and may result in your sample boiling over a range of temperatures.

## Formulations are Mixtures with Exact Amounts of Components

1) Formulations are useful mixtures with a precise purpose that are made by following a 'formula' (a recipe). Each component in a formulation is present in a measured quantity, and contributes to the properties of the formulation so that it meets its required function.

*Take a look at p.24 for more on mixtures.*

For example, paints are formulations composed of:

Pigment — gives the paint colour (for example titanium oxide is used as a pigment in white paints).

Solvent — used to dissolve the other components and alter the viscosity (runniness).

Binder (resin) — forms a film that holds the pigment in place after it's been painted on.

Additives — added to further change the physical and chemical properties of the paint.

Depending on the purpose of the paint, the chemicals used and their amounts will be changed so the paint produced is right for the job.

2) Formulations are really important in the pharmaceutical industry. For example, by altering the formulation of a pill, chemists can make sure it delivers the drug to the correct part of the body at the right concentration, that it's consumable and has a long enough shelf life.

3) In everyday life, formulations can be found in cleaning products, fuels, cosmetics, fertilisers, metal alloys (see p.60) and even food and drink.

4) When you buy a product, you might find that it has information about its composition on the packaging. For example, the ratio or percentage of each component. This tells you the product's a formulation. It also lets you choose a formulation with the right composition for your particular use.

## Make sure you can use data to identify pure and impure substances...

Knowing how pure a product is can be vital in industries such as pharmaceuticals and the food industry. Extra stuff in it by mistake could change the properties of the product, and even make it dangerous.

# Testing for Gases

Ahh... tests, glorious tests. Luckily, these aren't the kind of tests you have to <u>revise</u> for, but you should probably revise these tests for your exam — it's <u>swings</u> and <u>roundabouts</u> really...

## There are **Tests** for **Four Common Gases**

### 1) **Chlorine**

Chlorine <u>bleaches</u> damp <u>litmus paper</u>, turning it white. (If you use blue litmus paper it may turn <u>red</u> for a moment first though — that's because a solution of chlorine is <u>acidic</u>.)

Litmus paper

Chlorine

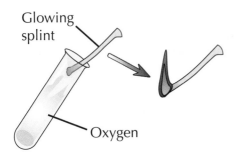
Glowing splint

Oxygen

### 2) **Oxygen**

If you put a glowing splint inside a test tube containing <u>oxygen</u>, the oxygen will <u>relight</u> the <u>glowing splint</u>.

### 3) **Carbon Dioxide**

Bubbling carbon dioxide through (or shaking carbon dioxide with) an aqueous solution of <u>calcium hydroxide</u> (known as <u>limewater</u>) causes the solution to turn <u>cloudy</u>.

$CO_2$ gas

Limewater

POP!
Lighted splint

$H_2$ gas

### 4) **Hydrogen**

If you hold a <u>burning splint</u> at the open end of a test tube containing hydrogen, you'll get a "<u>squeaky pop</u>". (The noise comes from the hydrogen burning quickly in the oxygen in the air to form water.)

---

PRACTICAL TIP

## These are all really useful tests to know...

The method you use to <u>collect a gas</u> will depend on whether it's <u>lighter</u> or <u>heavier</u> than <u>air</u>. If it's <u>heavier</u> (like chlorine), you have the test tube the <u>right way up</u> and the gas will <u>sink</u> to the bottom. If it's <u>lighter</u> (like hydrogen), you have the test tube <u>upside-down</u> and the gas will <u>rise</u> to fill it.

**Paper Chromatography**

You met chromatography on page 25. Now it's time to see <u>how it works</u>.

## Chromatography uses Two Phases

<u>Chromatography</u> is an analytical method used to <u>separate</u> the substances in a mixture. You can also use information from a chromatography experiment to help <u>identify</u> the substances that you have separated. There are different <u>types</u> of chromatography, but they all have two '<u>phases</u>':

> A <u>mobile phase</u> — where the molecules <u>can</u> move. This is always a <u>liquid</u> or a <u>gas</u>.
> A <u>stationary phase</u> — where the molecules <u>can't</u> move. This can be a <u>solid</u> or a really <u>thick liquid</u>.

1) During a chromatography experiment, the substances in the sample constantly <u>move</u> between the mobile and the stationary phases — an equilibrium is formed between the two phases.

2) The mobile phase moves through the stationary phase, and anything <u>dissolved</u> in the mobile phase moves with it.

3) How quickly a chemical <u>moves</u> depends on how it's '<u>distributed</u>' between the two phases — whether it spends more time in the mobile phase or the stationary phase.

4) The chemicals that <u>spend more time</u> in the <u>mobile phase</u> than the <u>stationary phase</u> will move further through the stationary phase.

5) The components in a mixture will <u>normally</u> separate through the stationary phase, so long as all the components spend <u>different</u> amounts of time in the mobile phase.

6) The separated components form <u>spots</u>. The number of spots formed may <u>change</u> in different solvents as the distribution of the chemical will change depending on the solvent.

7) A <u>pure</u> substance will only ever form <u>one spot</u> in any solvent, since there is only <u>one</u> substance in the sample.

---

### Paper Chromatography

In <u>paper chromatography</u> the stationary phase is the chromatography paper (often filter paper) and the mobile phase is the solvent (e.g. ethanol or water).

The amount of time the molecules spend in each <u>phase</u> depends on two things:

- How <u>soluble</u> they are in the solvent.
- How <u>attracted</u> they are to the paper.

Molecules with a <u>higher solubility</u> in the solvent, and which are <u>less attracted</u> to the paper, will spend <u>more time</u> in the <u>mobile phase</u> — and they'll be carried further up the paper.

The method for carrying out paper chromatography is on page 25.

---

## Chromatography revision — it's a phase you have to get through...

Chromatography works because each of the chemicals in a mixture spends different amounts of time dissolved in the <u>mobile phase</u> and stuck to the <u>stationary phase</u>. It's great — all you need is some <u>paper</u> and a bit of <u>solvent</u>. There's more about using it to <u>identify</u> chemicals coming up on the next page.

# Paper Chromatography

Now that you know a bit of the <u>theory</u> behind how paper chromatography works, here's how you can use a <u>chromatogram</u> to analyse a particular substance and find out <u>what's in it</u>.

## You can Calculate the R$_f$ Value for Each Chemical

1) The result of chromatography analysis is called a <u>chromatogram</u>.

2) An <u>R$_f$ value</u> is the <u>ratio</u> between the distance travelled by the <u>dissolved substance</u> (the solute) and the distance travelled by the <u>solvent</u>.

3) You can calculate R$_f$ values using this <u>formula</u>:

$$R_f = \frac{\text{distance travelled by substance (B)}}{\text{distance travelled by solvent (A)}}$$

This is the distance from the baseline to the centre of the spot.

4) The <u>further</u> through the stationary phase a substance moves, the <u>larger</u> the R$_f$ value.

5) Chromatography is often carried out to see if a certain substance is present in a mixture. To do this, you run a <u>pure sample</u> of that substance (a reference) alongside the unknown mixture. If the R$_f$ values of the reference and one of the spots in the mixture <u>match</u>, the substance may be present (although you haven't yet proved they're the same).

## The R$_f$ Value is Affected by the Solvent

1) The <u>R$_f$ value</u> of a substance is <u>dependent</u> on the solvent you use — if you <u>change the solvent</u> the R$_f$ value for the substance will <u>change</u>.

2) You can test both the <u>mixture</u> and the <u>reference</u> in a number of <u>different</u> solvents.

3) If the R$_f$ value of the reference matches the R$_f$ value of one of the spots in the mixture in <u>all the solvents</u>, then it's likely the reference compound is <u>present</u> in the mixture.

4) If the spot in the mixture and the spot in the reference only have the same R$_f$ value in <u>some</u> of the solvents, then the reference compound <u>isn't</u> present in the mixture.

## You need to learn the formula for R$_f$

Sometimes, when you're doing paper chromatography, you'll end up with a spot left sitting on the <u>baseline</u>, even after your solvent has run all the way up the paper. Any substance that remains on the baseline is <u>insoluble</u> in that solvent — you could rerun the experiment using a different solvent to try and identify it.

# Warm-Up & Exam Questions

Look, a chromatography question — those things are fun.  Get your investigative hat on and get stuck in...

## Warm-Up Questions

1) What is meant by a pure substance in chemistry?
2) What effect will impurities in a substance have on its boiling point?
3) Give an example of a formulation used in everyday life.
4) What effect does chromatography have on a mixture?

## Exam Questions

**PRACTICAL**

**1** Electrolysis of water gives hydrogen gas and oxygen gas.

**1.1** Describe how you could identify hydrogen gas using a simple laboratory test.

*[2 marks]*

**1.2** Describe how you could identify oxygen gas using a simple laboratory test.

*[2 marks]*

**PRACTICAL**

**2** A scientist used chromatography to analyse the composition of five food colourings.  Four of the colourings were unknown (**A – D**).  The other was sunrise yellow.  The results are shown in **Figure 1**.

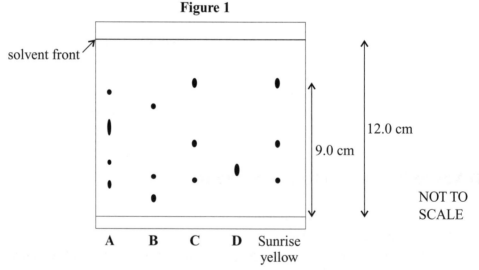

**Figure 1**

**2.1** Which food colouring is most likely to be a pure compound?

*[1 mark]*

**2.2** Which food colouring definitely contains at least four different compounds?

*[1 mark]*

**2.3** Which of the food colourings, **A-D**, could be the same as sunrise yellow?

*[1 mark]*

**2.4** Calculate the $R_f$ value for the spot of chemical in sunrise yellow which is furthest up the chromatogram.

*[2 marks]*

# Revision Summary for Topic 8

Here are some questions to work through before you get all geared up for Topic 9. By the time you're done you should know a few ways of determining the <u>components</u> of substances. I bet you can't wait...

- Try these questions and <u>tick off each one</u> when you <u>get it right</u>.
- When you've done <u>all the questions</u> under a heading and are <u>completely happy</u> with it, tick if off.

## Purity and Formulations (p.122) ☑

1) Describe how you could test the purity of a sample of a chemical. ☑
2) What effect will impurities in a substance have on its melting point? ☑
3) What is a formulation? ☑

## Testing for Gases (p.123) ☑

4) Describe the test for chlorine gas. ☑
5) Describe the test for carbon dioxide. ☑

## Paper Chromatography (p.124-125) ☑

6) What are the two phases called in chromatography? ☑
7) In paper chromatography, how many spots will a pure substance form on the paper? ☑
8) Give two factors which affect the amount of time a chemical spends in each of the two phases during a paper chromatography experiment. ☑
9) Draw and label a diagram of the set-up you would use to carry out a paper chromatography experiment.
10) What is the solvent front on a chromatogram? ☑
11) What does an $R_f$ value represent? ☑
12) Give the formula for working out the $R_f$ value of a substance. ☑
13) Which will have a larger $R_f$ value — a substance that has moved a long way along the chromatogram, or one that remains nearer the origin? ☑
14) Explain how you can use paper chromatography to identify if a certain substance is present in a mixture. ☑
15) Would you expect the $R_f$ value of a substance to change if you changed the solvent used in a paper chromatography experiment? ☑

# The Evolution of the Atmosphere

Theories for how the Earth's atmosphere <u>evolved</u> have changed a lot over the years — it's hard to gather evidence from such a <u>long time period</u> and from <u>so long ago</u> (4.6 billion years).  Here is one idea we've got:

## Phase 1 — **Volcanoes** Gave Out **Gases**

1)  The first <u>billion years</u> of Earth's history were pretty explosive — the surface was covered in <u>volcanoes</u> that erupted and released lots of gases.

2)  We think this was how the <u>early atmosphere</u> was formed.

3)  The early atmosphere was probably mostly made up of <u>carbon dioxide</u>, with <u>virtually no oxygen</u>.  This is quite like the atmospheres of <u>Mars</u> and <u>Venus</u> today.

4)  Volcanic activity also released <u>nitrogen</u>, which built up in the atmosphere over time, as well as <u>water vapour</u> and small amounts of <u>methane</u> and <u>ammonia</u>.

## Phase 2 — **Oceans**, **Algae** and **Green Plants** Absorbed $CO_2$

1)  When the water vapour in the atmosphere <u>condensed</u>, it formed the <u>oceans</u>.

2)  Lots of carbon dioxide was removed from the early atmosphere as it <u>dissolved</u> in the oceans.  This dissolved carbon dioxide then went through a series of reactions to form <u>carbonate precipitates</u> that formed <u>sediments</u> on the <u>seabed</u>.

3)  Later, marine <u>animals</u> evolved.  Their <u>shells</u> and <u>skeletons</u> contained some of these <u>carbonates</u> from the oceans.

4)  <u>Green plants</u> and <u>algae</u> evolved and absorbed some of the carbon dioxide so that they could carry out <u>photosynthesis</u> (see next page).

## Before volcanic activity, the Earth didn't even have an atmosphere

One way scientists can get information about what Earth's <u>atmosphere</u> was like in the past is from <u>Antarctic ice cores</u>.  Each year a layer of <u>ice</u> forms with tiny <u>bubbles of air</u> trapped in it.  The <u>deeper</u> you go in the ice, the <u>older</u> the air.  So analysing bubbles from different layers shows you how the atmosphere has <u>changed</u>.

# The Evolution of the Atmosphere

## Some **Carbon** Became **Trapped** in **Fossil Fuels** and **Rocks**

Some of the carbon that organisms took in from the atmosphere and oceans became locked up in <u>rocks</u> and <u>fossil fuels</u> after the organisms died.

1) When plants, plankton and marine animals <u>die</u>, they fall to the seabed and get <u>buried</u> by <u>layers of sediment</u>.

2) Over millions of years, they become <u>compressed</u> and form <u>sedimentary rocks</u>, <u>oil</u> and <u>gas</u> — trapping the carbon within them (helping to keep it out of the atmosphere).

3) Things like coal, crude oil and natural gas that are made by this process are called '<u>fossil fuels</u>'.

4) <u>Crude oil</u> and <u>natural gas</u> are formed from deposits of <u>plankton</u>. These fossil fuels form reservoirs under the seabed when they get <u>trapped</u> in rocks.

5) <u>Coal</u> is a sedimentary rock made from thick <u>plant deposits</u>.

6) <u>Limestone</u> is also a sedimentary rock. It's mostly made of <u>calcium carbonate</u> deposits from the <u>shells</u> and <u>skeletons</u> of marine organisms.

*The shells of marine organisms like this one are made of calcium carbonate. They form deposits on the seabed when the organism dies.*

## Phase 3 — Green Plants and Algae **Produced Oxygen**

1) As well as absorbing the carbon dioxide in the atmosphere, green plants and algae produced oxygen by <u>photosynthesis</u> — this is when plants use light to convert carbon dioxide and water into <u>sugars</u>:

$$\text{carbon dioxide} \; + \; \text{water} \; \xrightarrow{\text{light}} \; \text{glucose} \; + \; \text{oxygen}$$
$$6CO_2 \quad + \quad 6H_2O \; \xrightarrow{} \; C_6H_{12}O_6 \; + \quad 6O_2$$

2) Algae evolved <u>first</u> — about <u>2.7 billion</u> years ago.

3) Then over the next <u>billion years</u> or so, green plants also evolved.

4) As oxygen levels built up in the atmosphere over time, more <u>complex life</u> (like animals) could evolve.

5) Eventually, about <u>200 million years ago</u>, the atmosphere reached a composition similar to how it is <u>today</u>:

- approximately <u>80% nitrogen</u>,
- approximately <u>20% oxygen</u>,
- small amounts of other gases (each making up <u>less than 1%</u> of the atmosphere), mainly <u>carbon dioxide</u>, <u>noble gases</u> and <u>water vapour</u>.

## Not too much $CO_2$ and enough $O_2$ — just right for complex life

Another way that scientists can work out what the <u>atmosphere</u> was like billions of years ago is to look at the <u>chemical composition</u> of <u>rocks</u>. They can also look for the appearance of different <u>organisms</u> in the <u>fossil record</u> (including plants and algae) to try to work out what might have caused the changes they see.

# Climate Change and Greenhouse Gases

Greenhouse gases are important, but can also cause <u>problems</u> — it's all about keeping a delicate <u>balance</u>.

## Carbon Dioxide is a Greenhouse Gas

1) Greenhouse gases like <u>carbon dioxide</u>, <u>methane</u> and <u>water vapour</u> act like an insulating layer in the Earth's atmosphere — this, amongst other factors, allows the Earth to be <u>warm</u> enough to support <u>life</u>.

2) All particles <u>absorb</u> certain frequencies of radiation. Greenhouse gases <u>don't</u> absorb the <u>incoming short wavelength</u> radiation from the Sun — but they <u>do</u> absorb the <u>long wavelength radiation</u> that gets reflected back off the Earth.

3) Then they <u>re-radiate</u> it in all directions — including <u>back towards the Earth</u>.

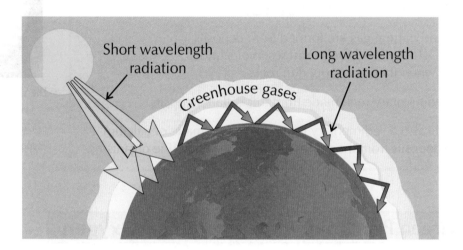

4) The longwave radiation is <u>thermal radiation,</u> so it results in <u>warming</u> of the surface of the Earth. This is the <u>greenhouse effect</u>.

5) Some forms of <u>human activity</u> affect the amount of greenhouse gases in the atmosphere. For example:

> • <u>Deforestation</u> — fewer trees means less $CO_2$ is removed from the atmosphere via <u>photosynthesis</u>.
>
> • Burning <u>fossil fuels</u> — carbon that was 'locked up' in these fuels is <u>released</u> as $CO_2$.
>
> • <u>Agriculture</u> — more <u>farm animals</u> produce more <u>methane</u> through their digestive processes.
>
> • <u>Creating waste</u> — more <u>landfill sites</u> and more waste from <u>agriculture</u> means more $CO_2$ and methane released by <u>decomposition</u> of waste.

## Greenhouse gases aren't all bad news — we need them to survive

Without greenhouse gases our planet would be incredibly <u>cold</u> — the greenhouse effect warms the Earth enough for it to support <u>living things</u>. Without it we wouldn't be here. But the overall <u>balance</u> of gases in the atmosphere matters — you can have too much of a good thing, as you're about to find out...

# Climate Change and Greenhouse Gases

## Increasing Carbon Dioxide is Linked to Climate Change

1) The Earth's temperature does <u>vary naturally</u>.

2) But recently, the average temperature of the Earth's surface has been <u>increasing</u> by amounts that are greater than we would expect to see naturally. Most scientists agree that the extra carbon dioxide from <u>human activity</u> is causing this increase, and that increasing global temperature will lead to <u>climate change</u>.

3) Evidence for this has been <u>peer-reviewed</u> (see page 1) — so you know that this information is <u>reliable</u>.

4) Unfortunately, it's hard to <u>fully understand</u> the Earth's climate — this is because it's so <u>complex</u>, and there are so many <u>variables</u>, that it's very hard to make a <u>model</u> that isn't <u>oversimplified</u>.

5) This has led to <u>speculation</u> about the link between carbon dioxide and climate change, particularly in the <u>media</u> (where stories may be <u>biased</u>, or only <u>some</u> of the information given).

See page 2 for more on science in the media.

## Climate Change Could Have Dangerous Consequences

The Earth's climate is <u>complex</u>, but it's still important to make <u>predictions</u> about the <u>consequences</u> of climate change so that policy-makers can make decisions <u>now</u>. For example:

1) An increase in global temperature could lead to polar ice caps <u>melting</u> — causing a <u>rise</u> in <u>sea levels</u>, <u>increased flooding</u> in coastal areas and <u>coastal erosion</u>.

2) Changes in <u>rainfall patterns</u> (the amount, timing and distribution) may cause some regions to get <u>too much</u> or <u>too little</u> water. This, along with changes in <u>temperature</u>, may affect the ability of certain regions to <u>produce food</u>.

3) The <u>frequency</u> and <u>severity</u> of <u>storms</u> may also <u>increase</u>.

4) Changes in <u>temperature</u> and the <u>amount of water</u> available in a habitat may affect <u>wild species</u>, leading to differences in their <u>distribution</u>.

## People can get quite hot under the collar talking about all this...

That's because climate change could have a <u>massive impact</u> on many people's lives across the world. It's really important that we understand what <u>causes</u> it, as well as how to prevent any <u>damaging consequences</u>.

# Carbon Footprints

It's generally accepted that greenhouse gas emissions from <u>human activities</u> are causing <u>climate change</u>. Knowing what causes the <u>biggest</u> emissions of carbon dioxide could help us focus our efforts to <u>reduce</u> them.

## Carbon Footprints are Tricky to Measure

1) Carbon footprints are basically a <u>measure</u> of the amount of <u>carbon dioxide</u> and other <u>greenhouse gases</u> released over the <u>full life cycle</u> of something.

2) That something could be a <u>service</u> (e.g. the school bus), an <u>event</u> (e.g. the Olympics), a <u>product</u> (e.g. a toastie maker) — almost <u>anything</u>.

3) <u>Measuring</u> the total carbon footprint of something can be <u>very hard</u>, though — or even <u>impossible</u>.

4) That's because there are so many <u>different factors</u> to consider — for example, you would have to count the emissions released as a result of <u>manufacturing all the parts</u> of your toastie maker and in <u>making it</u>, not to mention the emissions produced when you <u>actually use it</u> and finally <u>dispose</u> of it.

5) Still, a <u>rough calculation</u> can give a good idea of what the <u>worst emitters</u> are, so that people can <u>avoid them</u> in the future.

## There are Ways of Reducing Carbon Footprints

You can't always measure a carbon footprint <u>exactly</u>, but there are always ways to <u>reduce it</u>.

Anything that <u>reduces</u> the amount of <u>greenhouse gases</u> (e.g. carbon dioxide or methane) given out by a process will also reduce its carbon footprint. Here are some things that can be done:

1) <u>Renewable energy sources</u> or <u>nuclear energy</u> could be used instead of <u>fossil fuels</u>.

2) Using more <u>efficient processes</u> could <u>conserve energy</u> and cut <u>waste</u>. Lots of waste <u>decomposes</u> to release <u>methane</u>, so this will reduce methane emissions.

3) Governments could <u>tax</u> companies or individuals based on the amount of greenhouse gases they <u>emit</u> — e.g. taxing <u>cars</u> based on the amount of <u>carbon dioxide</u> they emit over a set distance could mean that people <u>choose</u> to buy cars that are more <u>fuel-efficient</u> and so less polluting.

4) Governments can also put a <u>cap</u> on emissions of <u>all</u> greenhouse gases that companies make — then <u>sell licences</u> for emissions <u>up to</u> that cap.

5) There's also technology that <u>captures</u> the $CO_2$ produced by burning fossil fuels <u>before</u> it's released into the atmosphere — it can then be <u>stored deep underground</u> in cracks in the rock, such as old <u>oil wells</u>.

# Carbon Footprints

## But Making **Reductions** is **Still Difficult**

1) It's easy enough <u>saying</u> that we should cut emissions, but <u>actually doing it</u> — that's a <u>different story</u>.

2) For a start, there's still a lot of work to be done on <u>alternative technologies</u> that result in <u>lower</u> $CO_2$ emissions. For example:

- <u>Carbon capture and storage</u> (see previous page) is a relatively new idea. At the moment the technology is still at the <u>developmental stage</u>.
- Many renewable energy technologies, e.g. solar panels, are still quite <u>expensive</u>. More <u>development</u> should make them <u>cheaper</u>, so they can be used more <u>widely</u>.

3) A lot of <u>governments</u> are also worried that making changes to reduce carbon dioxide emissions could have an impact on the <u>economic growth</u> of their countries — which could be <u>bad</u> for people's <u>well-being</u>. This is particularly important for countries that are <u>still developing</u>.

Forests take in carbon dioxide and burning trees releases carbon dioxide. So preventing deforestation can help to cut a country's carbon footprint.

4) Because not everyone is on board, it's hard to make <u>international agreements</u> to reduce emissions. Most countries don't want to <u>sacrifice</u> their <u>economic development</u> if they think that others <u>won't do the same</u>.

5) It's not just governments, though — <u>individuals</u> (particularly those in developed countries) need to make changes to their <u>lifestyles</u>. For example:

An individual can <u>reduce</u> their <u>personal carbon footprint</u> by:
- choosing to <u>cycle</u> or <u>walk</u> instead of using a <u>car</u>,
- reducing how much they use <u>air travel</u>,
- doing anything that <u>saves energy</u> at home (e.g. turning heating down).

6) But it might be <u>hard</u> to get people to make changes if they <u>don't want to</u> and if there isn't <u>enough education</u> provided about <u>why</u> the changes are necessary and <u>how</u> to make them.

## Lifestyle changes can be tough, but they might be essential in future

You need to be able to describe how <u>carbon footprints</u> could be <u>reduced</u> — don't forget that <u>governments</u>, as well as <u>individuals</u>, can take actions to reduce carbon emissions. Make sure that you can also give reasons why it can be hard to get <u>countries</u> and <u>people</u> to take actions to reduce their carbon footprints.

# Air Pollution

Increasing carbon dioxide is causing climate change. But $CO_2$ isn't the only gas released when fossil fuels burn — you also get other nasty gases, like oxides of nitrogen, sulfur dioxide and carbon monoxide.

## Combustion of Fossil Fuels Releases Gases and Particles

1) Fossil fuels, such as crude oil and coal, contain hydrocarbons. During combustion, the carbon and hydrogen in these compounds are oxidised, so that carbon dioxide and water vapour are released back into the atmosphere.

Hydrocarbons are compounds that only contain hydrogen and carbon (see p.115).

2) When there's plenty of oxygen, all the fuel burns — this is called complete combustion.

3) If there's not enough oxygen, some of the fuel doesn't burn — this is called incomplete combustion. Under these conditions, solid particles (called particulates), made up of soot (carbon) and unburned hydrocarbons, are released and carbon monoxide can be produced as well as carbon dioxide.

4) Particulates in the air can cause all sorts of problems:

- If particulates are inhaled, they can get stuck in the lungs and cause damage. This can then lead to respiratory problems.
- They're bad for the environment too. Particulates (and the clouds they help to produce), reflect sunlight back into space. This means that less light reaches the Earth, causing global dimming.

5) It's not just particulates from incomplete combustion that cause problems. Carbon monoxide is pretty nasty too.

There's more about complete combustion on p.116 and incomplete combustion on p.134.

- Carbon monoxide (CO) is really dangerous because it can stop your blood from doing its job of carrying oxygen around the body.
- It does this by binding to the haemoglobin in your blood that normally carries $O_2$ — so less oxygen is able to be transported round your body.
- A lack of oxygen in the blood can lead to fainting, a coma or even death.
- Carbon monoxide doesn't have any colour or smell, so it's very hard to detect. This makes it even more dangerous.

## Sulfur Dioxide and Oxides of Nitrogen Can be Released

1) Sulfur dioxide ($SO_2$) is released during the combustion of fossil fuels, such as coal, that contain sulfur impurities — the sulfur in the fuel becomes oxidised.

2) Nitrogen oxides are created from a reaction between the nitrogen and oxygen in the air, caused by the heat of burning. (This can happen in the internal combustion engines of cars.)

3) When these gases mix with water in clouds they form dilute sulfuric acid or dilute nitric acid. This then falls as acid rain.

4) Acid rain kills plants and damages buildings and statues. It also makes metal corrode.

5) Not only that, but sulfur dioxide and nitrogen oxides can also be bad for human health — they cause respiratory problems if they're breathed in.

You can test for sulfur impurities in a fuel by bubbling the gases from combustion through universal indicator solution. If the fuel contains sulfur, the gases will contain $SO_2$, which will form sulfuric acid and turn the universal indicator red.

# Fossil fuels are bad news — but we depend on them for many things...

...so a big reduction in their use is likely to be hard to achieve. Make sure you know the different pollutants that are given out when fuels burn, as well as the differences between complete and incomplete combustion.

# Warm-Up & Exam Questions

There's lots of important information in this section, from the Earth's atmosphere to climate change and pollution. Answer these questions to see what you can remember and what you need to go over again.

## Warm-Up Questions

1) Where do scientists think the gases that made up Earth's early atmosphere came from?
2) Give an example of a sedimentary rock.
3) Give an example of a fossil fuel.
4) Suggest one way that an individual could reduce their personal carbon footprint.
5) Name two potential pollutants that could be released as a result of incomplete combustion of hydrocarbons, that wouldn't be released as a result of complete combustion.

## Exam Questions

**1**  Use words from the box to complete the sentences below. *(Grade 4-6)*

| oxygen | carbon | carbon dioxide | photosynthesis | respiration |

Once green plants had evolved, they thrived in Earth's early atmosphere which was rich in
........................... . These plants also produced ........................... by the process of ........................... .
Some of the ........................... from dead plants eventually became 'locked up' in fossil fuels.

*[4 marks]*

**2**  Burning fossil fuels can produce pollutants like carbon dioxide, sulfur dioxide and particulate matter. *(Grade 6-7)*

**2.1**  Describe how sulfur dioxide can cause acid rain.

*[2 marks]*

**2.2**  Give **one** environmental problem caused by acid rain.

*[1 mark]*

**2.3**  Explain how burning fossil fuels can lead to global dimming.

*[3 marks]*

**2.4**  Carbon dioxide is a greenhouse gas. Describe how the greenhouse effect is responsible for warming the surface of the Earth.

*[4 marks]*

**3**  Many people believe that it is necessary for individuals to reduce their carbon footprints in order to prevent climate change from happening in the future. *(Grade 7-9)*

**3.1**  Define the term 'carbon footprint'.

*[1 mark]*

**3.2***  Describe some of the effects that an increase in global temperature could have on the environment. Explain the impact these effects may have on humans.

*[6 marks]*

# Revision Summary for Topic 9

That's all for Topic 9, but before you breathe a sigh of relief, there are some questions to get through.

- Try these questions and tick off each one when you get it right.
- When you've done all the questions under a heading and are completely happy with it, tick it off.

## The Evolution of the Atmosphere (p.128-129) ☑

1) Scientists believe that the early atmosphere was mostly carbon dioxide. Describe how the level of carbon dioxide in the atmosphere was reduced. ☑

2) Name four gases, other than carbon dioxide, that scientists think were present in the early atmosphere. ☑

3) Describe how limestone was formed from organisms millions of years ago. ☑

4) Write the balanced chemical equation for photosynthesis. ☑

5) State the approximate composition of the atmosphere today. ☑

## Climate Change and Greenhouse Gases (p.130-131) ☑

6) Name three greenhouse gases. ☑

7) Explain how the greenhouse effect keeps the Earth warm. ☑

8) State three ways in which human activity is leading to an increase in carbon dioxide in the atmosphere. ☑

9) Describe the recent trend that scientists have linked to increasing levels of carbon dioxide in the Earth's atmosphere. ☑

## Carbon Footprints (p.132-133) ☑

10) Give two ways in which a government could act to try to reduce the carbon footprints of companies in their country. ☑

11) Explain why it can be difficult to persuade countries to reduce their carbon dioxide emissions. ☑

## Air Pollution (p.134) ☑

12) Describe how the following air pollutants are produced:
   a) particulates,
   b) carbon monoxide,
   c) sulfur dioxide,
   d) nitrogen oxides. ☑

13) Why is carbon monoxide dangerous? ☑

14) Describe a test that you could use to detect sulfur impurities in a fuel. ☑

15) Apart from acid rain, give one other problem which may be caused by sulfur dioxide and nitrogen oxides. ☑

# Finite and Renewable Resources

There are lots of different resources that humans use to provide <u>energy</u> for things like <u>heating</u> or <u>travelling</u>, as well as for <u>building materials</u> and <u>food</u>.  Unfortunately, some of these resources will <u>run out</u> one day.

## Natural Resources Come From the Earth, Sea and Air

1) Natural resources form without <u>human input</u>.  They include anything that comes from the earth, sea or air.  For example, cotton for clothing or oil for fuel.

2) Some of these natural products can be <u>replaced</u> by synthetic products or <u>improved upon</u> by man-made processes.  For example, <u>rubber</u> is a natural product that can be extracted from the sap of a tree, however man-made <u>polymers</u> have now been made which can <u>replace</u> rubber in uses such as tyres.

3) <u>Agriculture</u> provides <u>conditions</u> where <u>natural resources</u> can be enhanced for our needs. E.g. the development of fertilisers have meant we can produce a high yield of crops.

## Some Natural Resources will Run Out

1) <u>Renewable resources</u> reform at a similar rate to, or faster than, we use them.

2) For example, timber is a renewable resource as <u>trees</u> can be planted following a harvest and only take a few years to regrow.  Other examples of renewable resources include <u>fresh water</u> and <u>food</u>.

3) <u>Finite (non-renewable) resources</u>, aren't formed quickly enough to be considered replaceable.

4) Finite resources include <u>fossil fuels</u> and <u>nuclear fuels</u> such as <u>uranium</u> and <u>plutonium</u>. <u>Minerals</u> and <u>metals</u> found in <u>ores</u> in the earth are also non-renewable materials.

5) After they've been <u>extracted</u>, many finite resources undergo <u>man-made processes</u> to provide fuels and materials necessary for modern life.  E.g. crude oil can undergo <u>fractional distillation</u> (see p.117) to produce products such as petrol, and metal ores can be <u>reduced</u> to produce pure metals (see p.84).

## Tables, Charts and Graphs Give You an Insight Into Different Resources

You may be asked to <u>interpret</u> information about resources in the exam.

**EXAMPLE:** **The table below shows information for two resources, coal and timber. Identify which resource is which.**

The time it takes for Resource 1 to reform is $10^5$ times shorter than Resource 2 suggesting it is a renewable resource.  Resource 1 also has a much lower energy density than Resource 2, so is more likely to be timber than coal. Resource 1 is timber and Resource 2 is coal.

| | Energy Density (MJ/m³) | Time it takes to form |
|---|---|---|
| **Resource 1** | 7 600-11 400 | 10 years |
| **Resource 2** | 23 000-26 000 | $10^6$ years |

$10^6$ is a shorthand way of showing 1 000 000.  This is because $10^6 = 10 \times 10 \times 10 \times 10 \times 10 \times 10 = 1 000 000$.

## Extracting Finite Resources has Risks

1) Many modern materials are made from <u>raw</u>, <u>finite resources</u>, e.g. most plastics and building materials.

2) People have to balance the <u>social</u>, <u>economic</u> and <u>environmental</u> effects of extracting finite resources.

For example, mining metal ores is <u>good</u> because <u>useful products</u> can be made.  It also provides local people with <u>jobs</u> and brings <u>money</u> into the area.  However, mining ores is <u>bad for the environment</u> as it uses loads of energy, scars the landscape, produces lots of waste and destroys habitats.

## Natural resources can be either renewable or finite

Before you move on, make sure you <u>learn a few examples</u> of finite and renewable resources.

# Sustainability

Many materials used in the modern world are limited. Scientists are constantly trying to find new and improved ways to extract and use natural resources more sustainably.

## Chemistry is **Improving Sustainability**

1) Sustainable development is an approach to development that takes account of the needs of present society while not damaging the lives of future generations.

2) As you saw on the previous page, not all resources are renewable so it's unsustainable to keep using them.

3) As well as using resources, extracting resources can be unsustainable due to the amount of energy used and waste produced. Processing the resources into useful materials, such as glass or bricks, can be unsustainable too as the processes often use energy that's made from finite resources.

4) If people reduce how much they use of a finite resource, that resource is more likely to last longer. Reducing usage of these resources will also reduce the use of anything needed to produce them.

5) We can't stop using finite resources altogether, but chemists can develop and adapt processes that use lower amounts of finite resources and reduce damage to the environment. For example, chemists have developed catalysts that reduce the amount of energy required for certain industrial processes.

## **Copper-Rich** Ores are in **Short Supply**

1) Copper is a finite resource — the supply of copper-rich ores is limited.

2) One way to improve its sustainability is by extracting it from low-grade ores (ores without much copper in). Scientists are looking into new ways of doing this:

### Bioleaching

Bacteria are used to convert copper compounds in the ore into soluble copper compounds, separating out the copper from the ore in the process. The leachate (the solution produced by the process) contains copper ions, which can be extracted, e.g. by electrolysis see p.88) or displacement (see p.86) with a more reactive metal, e.g. scrap iron.

These methods can be used to extract other metals too.

### Phytomining

Phytomining involves growing plants in soil that contains copper. The plants can't use or get rid of the copper so it gradually builds up in the leaves. The plants can be harvested, dried and burned in a furnace. The ash contains soluble copper compounds from which copper can be extracted by electrolysis or displacement using scrap iron.

3) Traditional methods of copper mining are pretty damaging to the environment (see next page). These new methods of extraction have a much smaller impact, but the disadvantage is that they're slow.

## The extraction of resources can be unsustainable

If we keep using finite resources at the rate that we currently are, one day they will run out. We need to find alternatives for finite resources, but in the meantime we can use methods to make them last as long as possible. For example, bioleaching and phytomining are a way of making reserves of metal ores last longer.

# Recycling

Once an object made from a finite resource is worn out, it's usually <u>more sustainable</u> to <u>recycle</u> it than to use new raw materials to replace it. Read on to find out why...

## Recycling Metals is Important

1) <u>Mining</u> and <u>extracting</u> metals takes lots of <u>energy</u>, most of which comes from burning <u>fossil fuels</u>.

2) Recycling metals often uses much <u>less energy</u> than is needed to mine and extract new metal, <u>conserves</u> the finite amount of each metal in the earth and cuts down on the amount of <u>waste</u> getting sent to <u>landfill</u>.

*Recycling is a way to reduce our need for copper-rich ores.*

3) Metals are usually recycled by <u>melting</u> them and then <u>casting</u> them into the shape of the new product.

4) Depending on what the metal will be used for after recycling, the amount of <u>separation</u> required for recyclable metals can change. For example:

Waste steel and iron can be kept together as they can be both added to iron in a <u>blast furnace</u> to reduce the amount of iron ore required.

*A blast furnace is used to extract iron from its ore at a high temperature using carbon.*

## Glass can **Also** be **Recycled**

<u>Glass recycling</u> can help <u>sustainability</u> by reducing the amount of energy needed to make new glass products, and also the amount of waste created when used glass is thrown away.

1) <u>Glass bottles</u> can often be <u>reused</u> without reshaping.

2) Other forms of glass can't be reused so they're <u>recycled</u> instead. Usually the glass is separated by <u>colour</u> and <u>chemical composition</u> before being recycled.

3) The glass is crushed and then melted to be reshaped for use in glass products such as <u>bottles</u> or jars. It might also be used for a <u>different</u> purpose such as <u>insulating</u> glass wool for wall insulation in homes.

---

## Recycling is key to sustainability — it's useful in lots of ways...

Remember that recycling doesn't just reduce the use of raw materials, it reduces the amount of <u>energy</u> used, the amount of <u>damage</u> to the environment and the amount of <u>waste</u> produced.

# Life Cycle Assessments

If a company wants to manufacture a new product, they carry out a <u>life cycle assessment (LCA)</u>.

## Life Cycle Assessments Show Total Environmental Costs

1) A <u>life cycle assessment (LCA)</u> looks at every <u>stage</u> of a product's life to assess the <u>impact</u> it would have on the environment.

2) Here are the different stages that need to be considered:

### 1) Getting the Raw Materials

1) Extracting <u>raw materials</u> needed for a product can <u>damage</u> the local <u>environment</u>, for example, mining metals. Extraction can also result in pollution due to the amount of energy needed.

2) Raw materials often need to be <u>processed</u> to extract the desired materials and this often needs <u>large amounts</u> of energy. For example, extracting metals from ores or fractional distillation of crude oil.

### 2) Manufacturing and Packaging

1) <u>Manufacturing</u> products and their packaging can use a lot of <u>energy</u> resources and can also cause a lot of <u>pollution</u>. For example, <u>harmful fumes</u> such as carbon monoxide or hydrogen chloride.

2) You also need to think about any <u>waste</u> products and how to <u>dispose</u> of them. The chemical reactions used to make compounds from their raw materials can produce waste products. Some waste can be turned into other <u>useful chemicals</u>, reducing the amount that ends up polluting the environment.

### 4) Product Disposal

1) Products are often <u>disposed</u> of in <u>landfill</u> sites. This takes up space and <u>pollutes</u> land and water. E.g. paint may wash off a product in landfill and pollute a river.

2) <u>Energy</u> is used to <u>transport</u> waste to landfill, which causes <u>pollutants</u> to be released into the atmosphere.

3) Products might be <u>incinerated</u> (burnt), which causes air pollution.

### 3) Using the Product

1) The use of a product can damage the environment. For example, <u>burning fuels</u> releases <u>greenhouse gases</u> and other <u>harmful substances</u>. <u>Fertilisers</u> can <u>leach</u> into streams and rivers causing damage to <u>ecosystems</u>.

2) <u>How long</u> a product is used for or <u>how many uses</u> it gets is also a factor — products that need lots of energy to produce but are used for ages may mean <u>less waste</u> in the <u>long run</u>.

## LCAs look at the environmental impact of a product's entire life

Doing a life cycle assessment for a product can be a very <u>time consuming</u> and <u>expensive</u> process, as there is so much to take account of. Some things can only be <u>predicted</u>, for example, how a consumer will use a product. Get to grips with <u>each stage</u> and what factors have to be taken into account at every step.

# Life Cycle Assessments

## You Can **Compare** Life Cycle Assessments for **Plastic** and **Paper Bags**

The table below shows how you might carry out a LCA of plastic and paper bags.

| Life Cycle Assessment Stage | Plastic Bag | Paper Bag |
|---|---|---|
| **Raw Materials** | Crude oil | Timber |
| **Manufacturing and Packaging** | The compounds needed to make the plastic are extracted from crude oil by fractional distillation, followed by cracking and then polymerisation. Waste is reduced as the other fractions of crude oil have other uses. | Pulped timber is processed using lots of energy. Lots of waste is made. |
| **Using the Product** | Can be reused. Can be used for other things as well as shopping, for example bin liners. | Usually only used once. |
| **Product Disposal** | Recyclable but not biodegradable and will take up space in landfill and pollute land. | Biodegradable, non-toxic and can be recycled. |

Life cycle assessments have shown that even though plastic bags aren't biodegradable, they take less energy to make and have a longer lifespan than paper bags, so may be less harmful to the environment.

## There are **Problems** with **Life Cycle Assessments**

1) The use of energy, some natural resources and the amount of certain types of waste produced by a product over it's lifetime can be easily quantified. But the effect of some pollutants is harder to give a numerical value to. E.g. it's difficult to apply a value to the negative visual effects of plastic bags in the environment compared to paper ones.

2) So, producing an LCA is not an objective method as it takes into account the values of the person carrying out the assessment. This means LCAs can be biased.

3) Selective LCAs, which only show some of the impacts of a product on the environment, can also be biased as they can be written to deliberately support the claims of a company in order to give them positive advertising.

## LCAs aren't all they are cracked up to be...

In the exam, you may have to analyse LCAs comparing different products and come to a conclusion about which product is the most environmentally friendly. But don't forget that not all environmental impacts can be measured in an LCA. Also, the opinions of the assessors have an effect on the result of the assessment and the results can be misused to suit an organisations aims.

# Warm-Up & Exam Questions

That's some more revision done and dusted and now it's time to test yourself on how much you've taken in. Have a go at the questions on this page to see if you need to revisit some topics.

## Warm-Up Questions

1) Give an example of a natural resource which has been replaced by a man-made alternative.
2) What is sustainable development?
3) Give three positive effects of recycling metals.
4) What are the four stages that need to be considered to conduct a life cycle assessment?

## Exam Questions

**1** Natural resources are formed without human input and are used for construction, fuel and food. *(Grade 4-6)*

**1.1** What is a finite natural resource?
Tick **one** box.

A natural resource that can never be remade. ☐

A natural resource that will never run out. ☐

A natural resource that doesn't renew itself quickly enough to be considered replaceable. ☐

A natural resource that can only be used in certain conditions. ☐

*[1 mark]*

**1.2** Aluminium is used to make soft drink cans. Extracting aluminium is a very energy intensive process. Suggest **two** ways that the use of soft drink cans can be made more sustainable.

*[2 marks]*

**2** Copper needs to be extracted from its ore before it can be used. *(Grade 6-7)*

**2.1** Explain why scientists have developed ways of extracting copper from low-grade ores.

*[1 mark]*

**2.2** Copper can be extracted from low-grade ores by a process called bioleaching.
Explain how the process works.

*[2 marks]*

**2.3** Give **one** advantage of using processes such as bioleaching rather than traditional mining.

*[1 marks]*

**2.4** Give **one** disadvantage of using processes such as bioleaching rather than traditional mining.

*[1 mark]*

**3** A life cycle assessment looks at the environmental impact of a product over its lifetime. *(Grade 6-7)*

**3.1** Describe why it can be difficult to give a complete assessment of a product over its entire life cycle.

*[1 mark]*

**3.2** A company carried out a LCA on one of their products but didn't take into account its disposal. However, an independent LCA found the disposal of the product to have the greatest environmental impact of any part of the product's life cycle.
Suggest why the LCA performed by the company didn't include details of the disposal of the product.

*[2 marks]*

# Potable Water and Water Treatment

We all need safe drinking water.  The <u>way</u> that water's made safe depends on <u>local conditions</u>.

## Potable Water is Water You Can Drink

1) Potable water is water that's been <u>treated</u> or is naturally <u>safe</u> for <u>humans to drink</u> — it's <u>essential for life</u>.

2) Chemists wouldn't call it <u>pure</u>, though.  Pure water <u>only</u> contains $H_2O$ molecules whereas <u>potable water</u> can contain lots of other <u>dissolved substances</u>.

3) The important thing is that the <u>levels</u> of <u>dissolved salts</u> aren't <u>too high</u>, that it has a <u>pH</u> between <u>6.5</u> and <u>8.5</u> and also that there aren't any nasties (like <u>bacteria</u> or other <u>microbes</u>) swimming around in it.

## How Potable Water is Produced Depends on Where You Are

1) Rainwater is a type of <u>fresh water</u>.  Fresh water is water that doesn't have much dissolved in it.

2) When it rains, water can either collect as <u>surface water</u> (in lakes, rivers and reservoirs) or as <u>groundwater</u> (in rocks called <u>aquifers</u> that trap water underground).

3) In the UK, the <u>source</u> of fresh water used depends on <u>location</u>.  Surface water tends to <u>dry up</u> first, so in <u>warm areas</u>, e.g. the south-east, <u>most</u> of the domestic water supply comes from <u>groundwater</u>.

4) Even though it only has <u>low levels</u> of dissolved substances, water from these <u>fresh water sources</u> still needs to be <u>treated</u> to make it <u>safe</u> before it can be used.  This process includes:

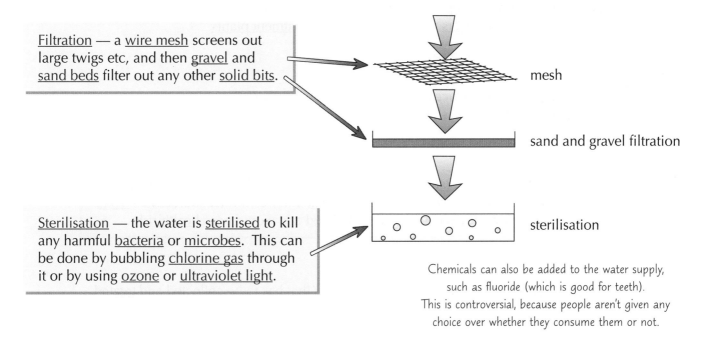

<u>Filtration</u> — a <u>wire mesh</u> screens out large twigs etc, and then <u>gravel</u> and <u>sand beds</u> filter out any other <u>solid bits</u>.

mesh

sand and gravel filtration

<u>Sterilisation</u> — the water is <u>sterilised</u> to kill any harmful <u>bacteria</u> or <u>microbes</u>.  This can be done by bubbling <u>chlorine gas</u> through it or by using <u>ozone</u> or <u>ultraviolet light</u>.

sterilisation

*Chemicals can also be added to the water supply, such as fluoride (which is good for teeth). This is controversial, because people aren't given any choice over whether they consume them or not.*

5) In some very <u>dry</u> countries, e.g. Kuwait, there's <u>not enough</u> surface or groundwater and instead <u>sea water</u> must be treated by <u>desalination</u> to provide potable water. In these countries <u>distillation</u> (see next page) can be used to <u>desalinate</u> sea water.

6) Sea water can also be treated by processes that use <u>membranes</u> — like <u>reverse osmosis</u>. The salty water is passed through a <u>membrane</u> that only allows water molecules to pass through. Ions and larger molecules are <u>trapped</u> by the membrane so <u>separated</u> from the water.

7) Both distillation and reverse osmosis need <u>loads of energy</u>, so they're really <u>expensive</u> and <u>not practical</u> for producing <u>large quantities</u> of fresh water.

# Potable Water and Water Treatment

## You can Test and Distil Water in the Lab

1) First, test the pH of the water using a <u>pH meter</u>. If the pH is too high or too low, you'll need to <u>neutralise</u> it by adding acid (if the pH is high) or alkali (if the pH is low). Use a pH meter to tell you when the solution is between <u>6.5 and 8.5</u>.

2) To distil the water, pour the salty water into a distillation apparatus, like the one on p.28. <u>Heat</u> the flask from below. The water will <u>boil</u> and form steam, leaving any dissolved salts in the flask. The steam will <u>condense</u> back to liquid water in the condenser and can be collected as it runs out.

3) Retest the <u>pH</u> of the water with a pH meter to check that it's between pH 6.5 and 8.5.

4) You can tell whether there were <u>salts</u> in the water by looking to see whether there are any <u>crystals</u> in the round bottomed flask once the water's been distilled.

## Waste Water Comes from Lots of Different Sources

1) We use water for lots of things at home — like <u>having a bath</u>, going to the <u>toilet</u>, doing the <u>washing-up</u>, etc. When you flush this water down the drain, it goes into the <u>sewers</u> and towards <u>sewage treatment plants</u>.

2) <u>Agricultural systems</u> also produce a lot of waste water including <u>nutrient run-off</u> from fields and <u>slurry</u> from animal farms.

3) Sewage from <u>domestic</u> or <u>agricultural</u> sources has to be <u>treated</u> to remove any <u>organic matter</u> and <u>harmful microbes</u> before it can be put <u>back</u> into fresh water sources like <u>rivers</u> or <u>lakes</u>. Otherwise it would make them very <u>polluted</u> and would pose <u>health risks</u>.

4) <u>Industrial processes</u> also produce a lot of waste water that has to be <u>collected</u> and <u>treated</u>.

5) As well as <u>organic matter</u>, industrial waste water can also contain <u>harmful chemicals</u> — so it has to undergo <u>additional stages</u> of treatment before it is safe to release it into the environment.

## The water that comes out of our taps has been treated

<u>Location</u> is a really important factor in determining <u>how</u> water is treated. For example, in the UK, there is a lot of <u>fresh water</u> available so this is filtered and then sterilised. However, in very <u>dry</u> countries a more <u>expensive</u> process may have to be used, such as the <u>distillation</u> or <u>reverse osmosis</u> of sea water.

# Potable Water and Water Treatment

It may not be glamourous but dealing with waste water is vital to stop us <u>polluting</u> our environment.

## Sewage **Treatment** Happens in **Several Stages**

Some of the <u>processes</u> involved in treating waste water at sewage treatment plants include:

1) Before being treated, the sewage is <u>screened</u> — this involves removing any <u>large bits</u> of material (like twigs or plastic bags) as well as any <u>grit</u>.

2) Then it's allowed to <u>stand</u> in a <u>settlement tank</u> and undergoes <u>sedimentation</u> — the <u>heavier</u> suspended solids sink to the bottom to produce <u>sludge</u> while the lighter <u>effluent</u> floats on the top.

   *<u>Aerobic</u> just means with oxygen, whereas <u>anaerobic</u> means without oxygen.*

3) The <u>effluent</u> in the settlement tank is <u>removed</u> and treated by <u>biological aerobic digestion</u>. This is when <u>air</u> is pumped through the water to encourage <u>aerobic bacteria</u> to break down any <u>organic matter</u> — including <u>other microbes</u> in the water.

4) The <u>sludge</u> from the bottom of the settlement tank is also removed and transferred into large <u>tanks</u>. Here it gets <u>broken down</u> by bacteria in a process called <u>anaerobic digestion</u>.

5) Anaerobic digestion breaks down the organic matter in the sludge, releasing <u>methane gas</u> in the process. The methane gas can be used as an <u>energy source</u> and the remaining digested waste can be used as a <u>fertiliser</u>.

6) For waste water containing <u>toxic substances</u>, additional stages of treatment may involve adding <u>chemicals</u> (e.g. to precipitate metals), <u>UV radiation</u> or using <u>membranes</u>.

Sewage treatment requires <u>more processes</u> than treating <u>fresh water</u> but uses <u>less energy</u> than the <u>desalination</u> of <u>salt water</u>, so could be used as an alternative in areas where there's not much fresh water. For example, <u>Singapore</u> is treating waste water and recycling it back into drinking supplies. However, some people don't like the idea of drinking water that used to be sewage.

 ## Waste water can be recycled to produce potable water
To learn the stages of water treatment, <u>cover</u> the diagram, <u>write out</u> each step and then <u>check</u> it.

# Warm-Up & Exam Questions

Now you know all there is to possibly know about water it's time to test yourself with some questions.

## Warm-Up Questions

1) Describe two features of potable water that make it safe for drinking.
2) What is the first step in treating fresh water?
3) In addition to organic matter, what else may have to be removed from industrial waste water?
4) What is produced following the sedimentation stage of water treatment?

## Exam Questions

1   **Figure 1** shows how water in some parts of the UK is treated during the production of potable water.  Grade 6-7

**Figure 1**

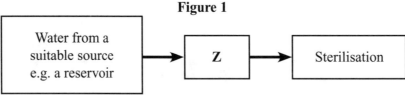

| Water from a suitable source e.g. a reservoir | → | **Z** | → | Sterilisation |

1.1   Describe the difference between potable water and pure water.

*[1 mark]*

1.2   Describe what happens during stage **Z** in **Figure 1**.

*[2 marks]*

1.3   Suggest **three** agents that could be used during the sterilisation stage of the process.

*[3 marks]*

2   Waste water from human activities must undergo treatment before being released into the environment. The stages of sewage treatment include screening, sedimentation, anaerobic digestion and aerobic digestion.  Grade 6-7

2.1   State the stage at which large pieces of material, such as twigs, are removed.

*[1 mark]*

2.2   During sedimentation, effluent is produced. Describe what happens during the next step in the treatment of effluent following sedimentation.

*[2 marks]*

2.3   In areas where fresh water is limited, treated waste water and sea water can be used as drinking water. Describe two disadvantages of using these processes compared to the treatment of fresh water.

*[2 marks]*

**PRACTICAL**

3   In some dry countries potable water is produced by the distillation of salt water. A student carries out distillation of salt water in the lab.  Grade 6-7

3.1   Describe **two** tests which can be used to determine whether or not the distilled water contains any sodium or chloride ions.

*[4 marks]*

3.2   Suggest a further test that would need to be carried out before the water could be considered potable.

*[1 mark]*

# Revision Summary for Topic 10

That wraps up Topic 10 — time to try these questions to see if you've got this topic in the bag.
- Try these questions and tick off each one when you get it right.
- When you've done all the questions under a heading and are completely happy with it, tick it off.

## Finite and Renewable Resources (p.137) ☐

1) What is meant by a natural resource? ☑
2) Give two examples of renewable resources. ☑
3) Give two examples of finite resources. ☑

## Sustainability and Recycling (p.138-139) ☐

4) Why can the extraction of resources be unsustainable? ☑
5) State two methods that can be used to extract copper from low grade ores. ☑
6) Describe how metals are usually recycled. ☑
7) Other than recycling, how can the sustainability of glass bottles be improved? ☑

## Life Cycle Assessments (p.140-141) ☑

8) Describe what life cycle assessments (LCAs) do? ☑
9) Give two factors associated with the extraction of raw materials which
   might be considered when carrying out an LCA for a product. ☑

## Potable Water and Water Treatment (p.143-145) ☐

10) What is potable water? ☑
11) Suggest a source of fresh water. ☑
12) Fresh water sources are treated before being used for drinking water.
    Explain why fresh water needs to be sterilised to make it potable. ☑
13) Name a process that can be used to make seawater safe to drink. ☑
14) Name three different sources of waste water. ☑
15) Why is it important to treat waste water before releasing it into the environment? ☑
16) What two useful products can be obtained by the anaerobic digestion of sewage sludge? ☑

# Taking Measurements

You've got a few <u>practicals</u> that you need to know about for your exams. This section is full of lots of information and advice for how to carry out practicals <u>really well</u>. First up — <u>measuring</u> things...

## Three Ways to Measure **Liquids**

Read volume from here — the bottom of the meniscus.

There are a few methods you might use to measure the volume of a liquid. Whichever method you use, always read the volume from the <u>bottom of the meniscus</u> (the curved upper surface of the liquid) when it's at <u>eye level</u>.

pipette filler

<u>Pipettes</u> are long, narrow tubes that are used to suck up an <u>accurate</u> volume of liquid and <u>transfer</u> it to another container. A <u>pipette filler</u> attached to the end of the pipette is used so that you can <u>safely control</u> the amount of liquid you're drawing up. Pipettes are often <u>calibrated</u> to allow for the fact that the last drop of liquid stays in the pipette when the liquid is ejected. This reduces <u>transfer errors</u>.

<u>Measuring cylinders</u> are the most common way to measure out a liquid. They come in all different <u>sizes</u>. Make sure you choose one that's the right size for the measurement you want to make. It's no good using a huge 1000 cm³ cylinder to measure out 2 cm³ of a liquid — the graduations will be too big, and you'll end up with <u>massive errors</u>. It'd be much better to use one that measures up to 10 cm³.

*If you only want a couple of drops of liquid, and don't need it to be accurately measured, you can use a dropping pipette to transfer it. For example, this is how you'd add a couple of drops of indicator into a mixture.*

## **Solids** Should Be Measured Using a **Balance**

1) To weigh a solid, start by putting the <u>container</u> you're weighing your substance <u>into</u> on the <u>balance</u>.

2) Set the balance to exactly <u>zero</u> and then start weighing out your substance.

3) It's <u>no good</u> carefully weighing out your solid if it's not all transferred to your reaction vessel — the amount in the <u>reaction vessel</u> won't be the same as your measurement. Here are a couple of methods you can use to make sure that none gets left in your weighing container...

- If you're <u>dissolving</u> the solid in a solvent to make a <u>solution</u>, you could <u>wash</u> any remaining solid into the new container using the <u>solvent</u>. This way you know that <u>all</u> the solid you weighed has been transferred.

- You could set the balance to <u>zero</u> before you put your <u>weighing container</u> on the balance. Then <u>reweigh</u> the weighing container <u>after</u> you've transferred the solid. Use the <u>difference</u> in mass to work out <u>exactly</u> how much solid you've transferred.

## Remember — always measure liquids at eye level

Measuring substances may not be the most exciting part of doing experiments, but remembering all the steps and doing it properly is really important if you want you results to be valid. The best kind of revision for these practical techniques is real <u>hands-on experience</u>.

# Taking Measurements

## Gas Syringes Measure Gas Volumes

1) Gases can be measured with a gas syringe.

2) They should be measured at <u>room temperature and pressure</u> as the <u>volume</u> of a gas <u>changes</u> with temperature and pressure.

3) You should also use a gas syringe that's the <u>right size</u> for the measurement you're making.

4) Before you use the syringe, you should make sure it's completely sealed and that the plunger moves smoothly.

## You May Have to Measure the **Time Taken** for a Change

1) You should use a <u>stopwatch</u> to <u>time</u> experiments. These measure to the nearest <u>0.1 s</u> so are <u>sensitive</u>.

2) Always make sure you <u>start</u> and <u>stop</u> the stopwatch at exactly the right time. For example, if you're investigating the rate of an experiment, you should start timing at the <u>exact moment</u> you mix the reagents and start the reaction. If you're measuring the time taken for a precipitate to form, you should watch the reaction like a hawk so you can <u>stop</u> timing the moment it goes cloudy.

## Measure **pH** to Find Out How **Acidic** or **Alkaline** a Solution Is

You need to be able to decide the best method for measuring pH, depending on what your experiment is.

1) <u>Indicators</u> are dyes that <u>change colour</u> depending on whether they're in an <u>acid</u> or an <u>alkali</u>. You use them by adding a couple of drops of the indicator to the solution you're interested in. They're useful for titration reactions, when you want to find the point at which a solution is neutralised.

2) <u>Universal indicator</u> is a <u>mixture</u> of indicators that changes colour <u>gradually</u> as pH changes. It doesn't show a <u>sudden</u> colour change. It's useful for <u>estimating</u> the pH of a solution based on its colour.

3) Indicators can be soaked into <u>paper</u> and strips of this paper can be used for testing pH. If you use a dropping pipette to spot a small amount of a solution onto some indicator paper, it will <u>change colour</u> depending on the pH of the solution.

> - <u>Litmus paper</u> turns <u>red</u> in acidic conditions and <u>blue</u> in basic conditions.
> - <u>Universal indicator paper</u> can be used to <u>estimate</u> the pH based on its colour.

There's loads more about pH on page 77.

4) Indicator paper is useful when you <u>don't</u> want to change the colour of <u>all</u> of the substance, or if the substance is <u>already</u> coloured so might <u>obscure</u> the colour of the indicator. You can also hold a piece of <u>damp indicator paper</u> in a <u>gas sample</u> to test its pH.

5) <u>pH probes</u> are attached to pH meters which have a <u>digital display</u> that gives a <u>numerical</u> value for the pH of a solution. They're used to give an <u>accurate value</u> of pH.

---

## Have your stopwatch ready before you try to time something

To make sure your results can be <u>trusted</u> by other scientists, you have to make sure all your measurements are <u>accurate</u>. So make sure you learn all the tips on these two pages for improving accuracy — e.g. using the right size of gas syringe for the measurement you're taking.

# Safety and Heating Substances

Safety is really important when carrying out experiments. This is because experiments in chemistry can often involve using hazardous chemicals or heating substances. Read on to find out how to be safe in the lab.

## Be Careful When You **Handle** or **Mix** Substances

1) There are lots of hazards in chemistry experiments, so before you start any experiment, you should read any safety precautions to do with your method or the chemicals you're using.

2) The substances used in chemical reactions are often hazardous. For example, they might catch fire easily (they're flammable), or they might irritate or burn your skin if you come into contact with them.

3) Whenever you're doing an experiment, you should wear a lab coat, safety goggles and gloves.

4) Always be careful that the chemicals you're using aren't flammable before you go lighting any Bunsen burners, and make sure you're working in an area that's well ventilated.

5) If you're doing an experiment that might produce nasty gases (such as chlorine), you should carry out the experiment in a fume hood so that the gas can't escape out into the room you're working in.

6) Never directly touch any chemicals (even if you're wearing gloves). Use a spatula to transfer solids between containers. Carefully pour liquids between different containers, using a funnel to avoid spills.

7) Be careful when you're mixing chemicals, as a reaction might occur. If you're diluting a liquid, add the concentrated substance to the water (not the other way around) or the mixture could get very hot.

## The **Temperature** of **Water Baths** & **Electric Heaters** Can Be **Set**

1) A water bath is a container filled with water that can be heated to a specific temperature.

- Set the temperature on the water bath, and allow the water to heat up.
- Place the vessel containing your substance in the water bath using a pair of tongs.
- The level of the water outside the vessel should be just above the level of the substance inside the vessel.
- The substance will then be warmed to the same temperature as the water.
- As the substance in the vessel is surrounded by water, the heating is very even. Water boils at 100 °C though, so you can't use a water bath to heat something to a higher temperature than this — the water won't get hot enough.

reaction vessel

temperature control

Handle any glassware you've heated with tongs until you're sure it's cooled down.

2) Electric heaters are often made up of a metal plate that can be heated to a certain temperature. The vessel containing the substance you want to heat is placed on top of the hot plate. You can heat substances to higher temperatures than you can in a water bath but, as the vessel is only heated from below, you'll usually have to stir the substance inside to make sure it's heated evenly.

## Measure **Temperature** Accurately

You can use a thermometer to measure the temperature of a substance:

- Make sure the bulb of your thermometer is completely submerged in any mixture you're measuring.
- If you're taking an initial reading, you should wait for the temperature to stabilise first.
- Read your measurement off the scale on a thermometer at eye level to make sure it's correct.

# Heating Substances

Sometimes water baths and electric heaters aren't <u>appropriate</u> for what you want to do — e.g. if you want to heat a sample of a compound to see what <u>colour</u> flame it produces, you should use a <u>Bunsen burner</u> instead.

## Bunsen Burners Have a Naked **Flame**

1) Bunsen burners are good for heating things quickly. You can easily adjust how strongly they're heating.

2) But you need to be careful not to use them if you're heating <u>flammable</u> compounds as the flame means the substance would be at risk of <u>catching fire</u>.

3) Here's how to use a Bunsen burner:

1) Connect the Bunsen burner to a gas tap, and check that the hole is <u>closed</u>. Place it on a <u>heat-proof mat</u>.

2) Light a <u>splint</u> and hold it over the Bunsen burner. Now, turn on the gas. The Bunsen burner should light with a <u>yellow flame</u>.

3) The <u>more open</u> the hole is, the <u>more strongly</u> the Bunsen burner will heat your substance. Open the hole to the amount you want. As you open the hole more, the flame should turn more <u>blue</u>.

4) The <u>hottest</u> part of the flame is just above the <u>blue cone</u>, so you should heat things here.

5) If your Bunsen burner is alight but not heating anything, make sure you <u>close</u> the hole so that the flame becomes <u>yellow</u> and <u>clearly visible</u>.

6) If you're heating something so that the container (e.g. a test tube) is <u>in</u> the flame, you should hold the vessel at the <u>top</u>, furthest away from the substance (and so the flame) using a pair of <u>tongs</u>.

7) If you're heating something <u>over</u> the flame (e.g. an evaporating dish), you should put a <u>tripod and gauze</u> over the Bunsen burner before you light it, and place the vessel on this.

## You might not expect the blue flame to be hotter, but it is

As you can see, it's not just when you're heating substances that you have to be safe — you should also be careful, for example, when you're using <u>hazardous chemicals</u> or if chemical reactions are likely to give off a lot of <u>heat</u>. Always <u>read through</u> any safety precautions you're given carefully <u>before</u> you start, otherwise you might do something dangerous.

# Setting Up Equipment

Setting up the equipment for an experiment correctly is <u>important</u> if you want to take accurate measurements.

## To Collect **Gases**, the System Needs to be **Sealed**

1) There are times when you might want to <u>collect</u> the gas produced by a reaction. For example, to investigate the <u>rate</u> of reaction.

2) The most accurate way to measure the volume of a gas that's been produced is to collect it in a <u>gas syringe</u> (see pages 104 and 105).

delivery tube
collected gas
gas syringe
reaction mixture

3) You could also collect it by <u>displacing water</u> from a measuring cylinder. Here's how you do it...

1) Fill a <u>measuring cylinder</u> with <u>water</u>, and carefully place it <u>upside down</u> in a container of water.

2) Record the <u>initial level</u> of the water in the measuring cylinder.

3) Position a <u>delivery tube</u> coming <u>from</u> the reaction vessel so that it's <u>inside</u> the measuring cylinder, pointing upwards. Any gas that's produced will pass <u>through</u> the delivery tube and <u>into</u> the <u>measuring cylinder</u>. As the gas enters the measuring cylinder, the <u>water</u> is <u>pushed out</u>.

4) Record the <u>level of water</u> in the measuring cylinder and use this value, along with your <u>initial value</u>, to calculate the <u>volume</u> of gas produced.

collected gas
delivery tube
measuring cylinder filled with water and upturned in a beaker of water
reaction mixture

4) This method is <u>less accurate</u> than using a gas syringe to measure the volume of gas produced. This is because some gases can <u>dissolve</u> in water, so less gas ends up in the measuring cylinder than is <u>actually produced</u>.

5) If just want to <u>collect</u> a sample to test (and don't need to measure a volume), you can collect it over water as above using a <u>test tube</u>. Once the test tube is full of gas, you can stopper it and store the gas for later.

*If the delivery tube is underneath the measuring cylinder rather than inside it then some of the gas might escape out into the air.*

**EXAM TIP**

## You can test the gas you've collected to find out what it is

Having a <u>good knowledge</u> of practical techniques won't just make your investigations more reliable, it might <u>come in handy</u> for questions in your exams. It's possible that you could be asked to comment on how equipment has been set up, e.g. suggest improvements.

# Setting Up Equipment

Some experiments involve slightly more <u>complicated</u> equipment that might be less familiar to you. For example, <u>electrolysis</u> experiments use <u>electrodes</u> — this page shows you how to set them up.

## You May Have to **Identify** the **Products** of Electrolysis

There's more about electrolysis on p.88-91.

1) When you electrolyse an <u>aqueous solution</u>, the products of electrolysis will depend on how reactive the ions in the solution are compared to the $H^+$ and $OH^-$ ions that come from water.

2) At the <u>cathode</u> you'll either get a <u>pure metal</u> coating the electrode or bubbles of <u>hydrogen gas</u>.

3) At the <u>anode</u>, you'll get bubbles of <u>oxygen gas</u> unless a <u>halide ion</u> is present, when you'll get the <u>halogen</u>.

4) You may have to predict and identify what's been made in an electrolysis experiment. To do this, you need to be able to <u>set up the equipment</u> correctly so that you can <u>collect</u> any gas that's produced. The easiest way to collect the gas is in a <u>test tube</u>.

The tests for gases are described on page 123.

5) Here's how to set up the equipment...

inverted test tube filled with solution

gas produced at electrodes collecting inside test tubes

electrodes inside test tubes

power supply

electrolyte solution

## Make Sure You Can **Draw Diagrams** of Your Equipment

1) When you're writing out a <u>method</u> for your experiment, it's always a good idea to draw a <u>labelled diagram</u> showing how your apparatus will be <u>set up</u>.

2) The easiest way to do this is to use a scientific drawing, where each piece of apparatus is drawn as if you're looking at its <u>cross-section</u>. For example:

beaker    test tube    tripod    heat-proof mat    gauze    Bunsen burner

The pieces of glassware are drawn without tops so they aren't sealed. If you want to draw a closed system, remember to draw a bung in the top.

## These simple diagrams are clear and easy to draw

Have a go at <u>drawing out</u> some of the practical diagrams on these pages using a simplified cross-section drawing of each piece of equipment. It'll give you some practice at doing them and you can revise how to set up the experiments as well. Win-win.

# Practice Exams

Once you've been through all the questions in this book, you should feel pretty confident about the exams.
As final preparation, here is a set of **practice exams** to really get you set for the real thing. The time allowed for
each paper is 1 hour 15 minutes. These papers are designed to give you the best possible preparation for your exams.

CGP    Practice Exam Paper
GCSE Combined Science

# GCSE Combined Science
## Chemistry Paper 1
### *Higher Tier*

In addition to this paper you should have:
• A ruler.
• A calculator.
• A periodic table

| Centre name | | | | |
|---|---|---|---|---|
| Centre number | | | | |
| Candidate number | | | | |

**Time allowed:**
• 1 hour 15 minutes

| Surname |
|---|
| Other names |
| Candidate signature |

**Instructions to candidates**
• Write your name and other details in the spaces provided above.
• Answer **all** questions in the spaces provided.
• Do all rough work on the paper.
• Cross out any work you do not want to be marked.

**Information for candidates**
• The marks available are given in brackets at the end of each question.
• There are 70 marks available for this paper.
• You are allowed to use a calculator.
• You should use good English and present your answers in a clear and organised way.
• For Questions 2.4 and 5.2, ensure that your answers have a clear and logical structure, include the right scientific terms, spelt correctly, and include detailed, relevant information.

**Advice to candidates**
• In calculations show clearly how you worked out your answers.

| For examiner's use | | | | | | |
|---|---|---|---|---|---|---|
| Q | Attempt Nº | | | Q | Attempt Nº | |
| | 1 | 2 | 3 | | 1 | 2 | 3 |
| 1 | | | | 4 | | | |
| 2 | | | | 5 | | | |
| 3 | | | | 6 | | | |
| | | | | 7 | | | |
| Total | | | | | | | |

**1**     The elements in Group 1 of the periodic table are known as the alkali metals.

**1.1**   Group 1 metals can react with non-metals to form ionic compounds.
          What is the charge on a Group 1 ion in an ionic compound?
          Tick **one** box.

          ☐   +2

          ☐   +3

          ☐   −1

          ☐   +1

*[1 mark]*

A student watched his teacher carefully place small pieces of lithium, sodium and potassium into cold water.  His observations are recorded in **Table 1**.

**Table 1**

| Metal | Observations |
|---|---|
| lithium | Fizzes, moves across surface. |
| sodium | Fizzes strongly, moves quickly across surface, melts. |
| potassium | Fizzes violently, moves very quickly across surface, melts and a flame is seen. |

He decides that the order of reactivity of the three metals is:

- potassium (most reactive)

- sodium

- lithium (least reactive)

**1.2**   Give **two** pieces of evidence from **Table 1** that support the student's conclusion.

          .......................................................................................................................................................

          .......................................................................................................................................................

          .......................................................................................................................................................

          .......................................................................................................................................................

*[2 marks]*

**Question 1 continues on the next page**

**Turn over ▶**

**1.3** Explain the pattern of reactivity that the student has noticed
in terms of the outer electrons of the atoms.

.......................................................................................................................

.......................................................................................................................

.......................................................................................................................

.......................................................................................................................

*[3 marks]*

**1.4** Complete and balance the chemical equation
for the reaction between lithium and water.

$$2Li + 2H_2O \rightarrow ............................. + .............................$$

*[2 marks]*

**1.5** Choose the statement that explains why the solution produced
when lithium reacts with water is alkaline.
Tick **one** box.

☐ It contains lithium ions.

☐ It contains water.

☐ It contains an ionic compound.

☐ It contains hydroxide ions.

*[1 mark]*

**1.6** The nuclear symbol for an atom of fluorine is shown below.

$$^{19}_{9}F$$

How many protons, neutrons and electrons are there in this atom of fluorine?

Protons = ...............................................................................................

Neutrons = .............................................................................................

Electrons = ............................................................................................

*[3 marks]*

**2** The structure and bonding of elements and compounds affects their properties.

**2.1** Sodium and chlorine can react together to form an ionic compound (sodium chloride). **Figure 1**, below, is a dot and cross diagram illustrating this reaction.

Complete the right-hand side of **Figure 1** by adding the charges of both ions and adding the electrons to the outer shell of the chloride ion.

**Figure 1**

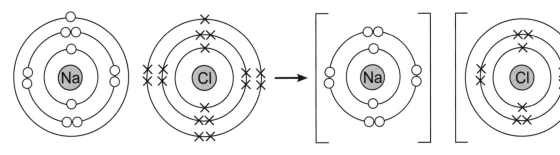

*[2 marks]*

**Table 2** shows some properties of five substances, **A-E**.

**Table 2**

| Substance | Melting point in °C | Boiling point in °C | Does it conduct electricity when solid? | Does it conduct electricity when dissolved or molten? |
|---|---|---|---|---|
| A | −210 | −196 | No | No |
| B | −219 | −183 | No | No |
| C | 801 | 1413 | No | Yes |
| D | 115 | 445 | No | No |
| E | 1083 | 2567 | Yes | Yes |

**2.2** Substance **A** consists of small, covalently bonded molecules.
Explain why it has a relatively low melting point.

................................................................................................................................

................................................................................................................................
*[2 marks]*

**2.3** Look at **Table 2**. One of the substances, **A-E**, is an ionic compound.
Use the information in the table to suggest which of the substances is ionic.
Explain your answer.

................................................................................................................................

................................................................................................................................

................................................................................................................................
*[2 marks]*

**Question 2 continues on the next page**

**Turn over ▶**

**2.4** **Table 3** contains information about some of the properties of diamond and graphite.

**Table 3**

|  | **Hardness** | **Melting point** | **Conducts electricity?** |
|---|---|---|---|
| **Diamond** | Hard | High | No |
| **Graphite** | Soft | High | Yes |

Explain these properties of diamond and graphite
in terms of their structure and bonding.

.......................................................................................................................................

.......................................................................................................................................

.......................................................................................................................................

.......................................................................................................................................

.......................................................................................................................................

.......................................................................................................................................

.......................................................................................................................................

.......................................................................................................................................

.......................................................................................................................................

.......................................................................................................................................

*[6 marks]*

**3**   **Figure 2** shows the apparatus used by a student to measure the temperature change that occurred when she added a piece of magnesium ribbon to dilute hydrochloric acid.

**Figure 2**

**3.1**   Suggest **two** changes that the student could make to the apparatus in order to reduce heat loss from her experiment.

........................................................................................................................................

........................................................................................................................................

........................................................................................................................................

........................................................................................................................................

*[2 marks]*

**3.2**   A close up of the thermometer used during the experiment is shown in **Figure 3.**

**Figure 3**

What value does each **small division** on the scale of the thermometer represent?
Tick **one** box.

☐   0.1 °C

☐   10 °C

☐   1 °C

☐   2 °C

*[1 mark]*

**Question 3 continues on the next page**

**Turn over ▶**

The student recorded the initial temperature of the dilute hydrochloric acid.
She added the magnesium ribbon to the acid. She then measured
the temperature of the reaction mixture every 10 seconds.
The student's results are shown on the graph in **Figure 4**.

**Figure 4**

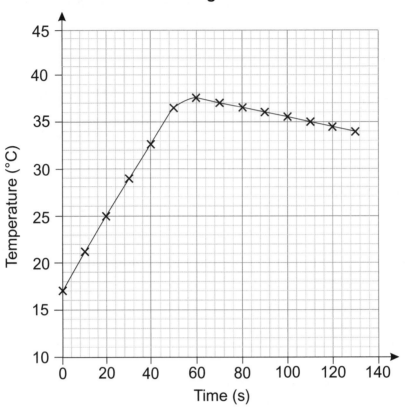

**3.3** Using the graph in **Figure 4**, give the highest temperature
of the mixture that the student recorded.

Highest temperature = ................. °C

*[1 mark]*

**3.4** The initial temperature of the acid was 17 °C.
Use this information and your answer from **3.3** to estimate
the total change in temperature of the reaction mixture.

.......................................................................................................................

Temperature change = ................ °C

*[2 marks]*

**3.5** State whether this reaction was exothermic or endothermic. Explain your answer.

.......................................................................................................................

.......................................................................................................................

*[1 mark]*

**4**     A student reacts four different metals with dilute sulfuric acid.
She controls all other variables to make sure that the test is fair.
She collects the hydrogen gas given off by each reaction in a gas syringe.
**Figure 5** shows all four reactions after 30 seconds.

### Figure 5

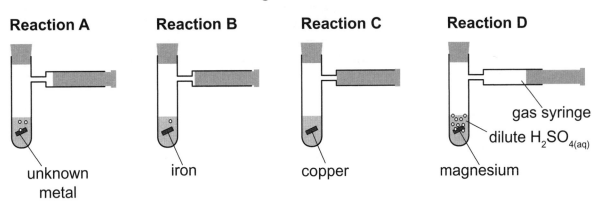

**4.1**     Which reaction, **A**, **B**, **C**, or **D**, contains the **most reactive** metal?
Explain how you can tell.

.....................................................................................................................................................

.....................................................................................................................................................

.....................................................................................................................................................

*[3 marks]*

**4.2**     Use your knowledge of the reactivity series to suggest a
possible identity for the unknown metal used in reaction **A**.

.....................................................................................................................................................

*[1 mark]*

**Question 4 continues on the next page**

**4.3** In another experiment, the student placed pieces of different metals in metal salt solutions. She left them for 10 minutes. The student then recorded whether any reaction had occurred. The results of this experiment are shown in **Table 4**.

**Table 4**

| | Did any reaction occur with: | | |
|---|---|---|---|
| | **iron sulfate** | **magnesium sulfate** | **copper sulfate** |
| **iron** | No | No | .................... |
| **magnesium** | .................... | No | Yes |
| **copper** | No | No | No |

Complete **Table 4** by filling in the gaps.

*[2 marks]*

**4.4** The equation for the reaction between magnesium and copper sulfate solution is:

$$Mg_{(s)} + CuSO_{4(aq)} \rightarrow MgSO_{4(aq)} + Cu_{(s)}$$

Write the ionic equation for this reaction.

....................................................................................................................................

*[2 marks]*

**5** A student added zinc oxide (ZnO) to dilute hydrochloric acid (HCl).
They reacted to produced zinc chloride, a soluble salt.

**5.1** Give the chemical formula of zinc chloride.

........................................................................................................................................

*[1 mark]*

**5.2** Describe a method that could be used to produce pure, dry crystals of zinc chloride.

........................................................................................................................................

........................................................................................................................................

........................................................................................................................................

........................................................................................................................................

........................................................................................................................................

........................................................................................................................................

........................................................................................................................................

........................................................................................................................................

........................................................................................................................................

........................................................................................................................................

........................................................................................................................................

........................................................................................................................................

........................................................................................................................................

*[6 marks]*

**5.3** Another student added solid sodium carbonate ($Na_2CO_3$) to dilute hydrochloric acid.
Name the salt formed by this reaction.

........................................................................................................................................

*[1 mark]*

**Question 5 continues on the next page**

**Turn over ▶**

**5.4**   Which gas was given off by the reaction described in **5.3**?
Tick **one** box.

☐   Hydrogen

☐   Oxygen

☐   Chlorine

☐   Carbon Dioxide

*[1 mark]*

**5.5**   The solution formed at the end of the reaction described in **5.3** is neutral.
Suggest a method you could use to test the pH of the solution.
State what you would expect to observe.

...............................................................................................................................

...............................................................................................................................

...............................................................................................................................

*[2 marks]*

**6** Iron can be extracted from iron(III) oxide, $Fe_2O_3$, by reduction, using carbon.
Here is the equation for this reaction:

$$2Fe_2O_3 + 3C \rightarrow 4Fe + 3CO_2$$

**6.1** Give **one** reason why this reaction is described as a reduction reaction.

..........................................................................................................................................
*[1 mark]*

**6.2** Calculate the mass of iron that could be extracted from 40 g of iron(III) oxide.
Relative atomic masses, $A_r$: Fe = 56, O = 16.

..........................................................................................................................................

..........................................................................................................................................

..........................................................................................................................................

..........................................................................................................................................

..........................................................................................................................................

Mass of iron = ............... g
*[4 marks]*

**6.3** Explain why reduction with carbon isn't used to extract aluminium from its ore.

..........................................................................................................................................

..........................................................................................................................................
*[2 marks]*

**6.4** Small amounts of carbon can be added to iron to make an alloy called steel.
Explain why steel is harder than pure iron.

..........................................................................................................................................

..........................................................................................................................................

..........................................................................................................................................

..........................................................................................................................................

..........................................................................................................................................

..........................................................................................................................................
*[4 marks]*

**Turn over for next question**

**Turn over ▶**

**7** A student carried out an experiment to investigate the electrolysis of copper sulfate solution, $CuSO_{4\ (aq)}$, using inert carbon electrodes. The diagram in **Figure 6** shows how his experiment was set up.

**Figure 6**

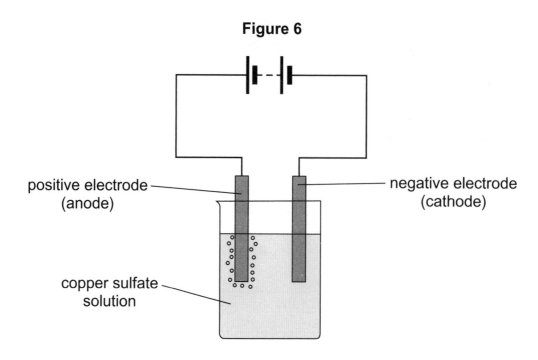

positive electrode (anode)

negative electrode (cathode)

copper sulfate solution

**7.1** Explain why a solution of copper sulfate can conduct electricity, but solid copper sulfate cannot.

.................................................................................................................................

.................................................................................................................................

*[2 marks]*

**7.2** List all **four** of the ions that are present in aqueous copper sulfate solution.

.................................................................................................................................

.................................................................................................................................

*[1 mark]*

**7.3** Complete the half equation shown below for the reaction taking place at the positive electrode (anode).

$$\text{....... } OH^- \rightarrow O_2 + \text{....... } H_2O + 4 \text{............}$$

*[1 mark]*

The student repeated the experiment three times, running the electrolysis for exactly 30 minutes each time. He weighed the dry electrodes before starting each run. At the end of each run, he dried both electrodes and weighed them again.

**Table 5** shows the change in mass of both electrodes for each of the three runs.

**Table 5**

| | Change in mass of electrode in g | | | |
|---|---|---|---|---|
| | **Run 1** | **Run 2** | **Run 3** | **Mean** |
| **Positive electrode (anode)** | 0.00 | 0.00 | 0.00 | 0.00 |
| **Negative electrode (cathode)** | 2.36 | 2.71 | 2.55 | .................. |

**7.4** Complete **Table 5** by finding the mean change in mass for the negative electrode.

*[1 mark]*

**7.5** Explain why the negative electrode increased in mass in this experiment. Your answer should include the half equation for the reaction taking place at the negative electrode.

...........................................................................................................................

...........................................................................................................................

...........................................................................................................................

...........................................................................................................................

...........................................................................................................................

*[3 marks]*

**7.6** The student decided to run the experiment for 60 minutes instead of 30 minutes. Predict the effect that this would have on the change in mass of the negative electrode.

...........................................................................................................................

*[1 mark]*

**END OF QUESTIONS**

# GCSE Combined Science

## Paper 2

## *Higher Tier*

In addition to this paper you should have:
*   A ruler.
*   A calculator.
*   A periodic table.

| Centre name | | | | |
|---|---|---|---|---|
| Centre number | | | | |
| Candidate number | | | | |

**Time allowed:**
*   1 hour 15 minutes

| Surname | |
|---|---|
| Other names | |
| Candidate signature | |

**Instructions to candidates**
*   Write your name and other details in the spaces provided above.
*   Answer **all** questions in the spaces provided.
*   Do all rough work on the paper.
*   Cross out any work you do not want to be marked.

**Information for candidates**
*   The marks available are given in brackets at the end of each question.
*   There are 70 marks available for this paper.
*   You are allowed to use a calculator.
*   You should use good English and present your answers in a clear and organised way.
*   For Questions 3.3 and 6.1, ensure that your answers have a clear and logical structure, include the right scientific terms, spelt correctly, and include detailed, relevant information.

**Advice to candidates**
*   In calculations show clearly how you worked out your answers.

**For examiner's use**

| Q | Attempt Nº | | | Q | Attempt Nº | | |
|---|---|---|---|---|---|---|---|
| | 1 | 2 | 3 | | 1 | 2 | 3 |
| 1 | | | | 5 | | | |
| 2 | | | | 6 | | | |
| 3 | | | | 7 | | | |
| 4 | | | | | | | |
| | | | Total | | | | |

**1** Alkanes are hydrocarbon compounds found in crude oil. **Table 1** shows how the boiling points of some alkanes change as the molecules get bigger.

**Table 1**

| Alkane | Molecular formula | Boiling point (°C) |
|--------|-------------------|--------------------|
| Propane | $C_3H_8$ | −42 |
| Butane | $C_4H_{10}$ | −0.5 |
| Pentane | $C_5H_{12}$ | |
| Hexane | $C_6H_{14}$ | 69 |
| Heptane | $C_7H_{16}$ | 98 |

**1.1** Using the data in **Table 1**, plot a graph of the number of carbon atoms in an alkane molecule against boiling point on the axes below.
Draw a smooth curve through the points you have plotted.

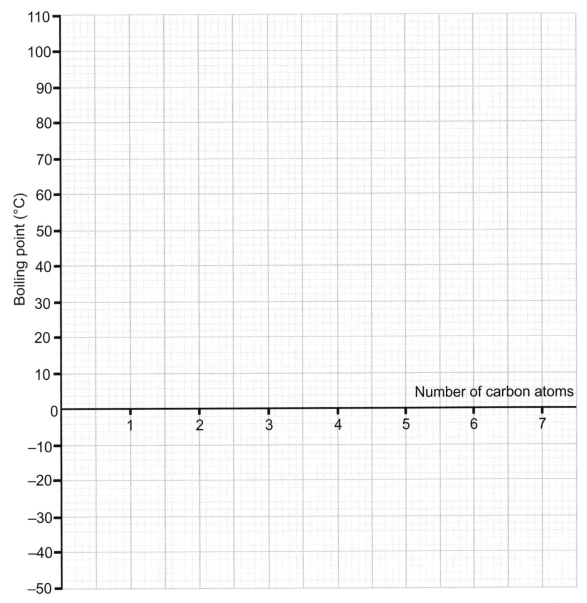

*[2 marks]*

**Turn over ▶**

**1.2** Use your graph to estimate the boiling point of pentane.

...................... °C

*[1 mark]*

**1.3** What is the general formula of the alkanes? Tick **one** box.

☐ $C_nH_{2n}$

☐ $C_nH_{2n+1}$

☐ $C_nH_{2n+2}$

☐ $C_nH_{2n-1}$

*[1 mark]*

**1.4** Propane is an alkane with three carbon atoms.
Draw the displayed formula of propane.

*[1 mark]*

**1.5** Propene is an alkene with three carbon atoms.
Describe a test you could use to distinguish between propene and propane.
Say what you would observe in each case.

................................................................................................................................

................................................................................................................................

................................................................................................................................

*[3 marks]*

**1.6** Propane burns in the presence of oxygen.
Complete this equation for the complete combustion of propane.

$$C_3H_8 + 5O_2 \rightarrow 3CO_2 + \text{...........................}$$

*[2 marks]*

**2** Nitrogen dioxide is an atmospheric pollutant that irritates the respiratory system. It is thought that there is a link between exposure to nitrogen dioxide and the severity of asthma attacks in people with asthma.

**Figure 1** shows the results of a study carried out by a group of scientists that compared atmospheric nitrogen dioxide levels with the severity of asthma attacks suffered by men under the age of 40 working in a city centre.

**Figure 1**

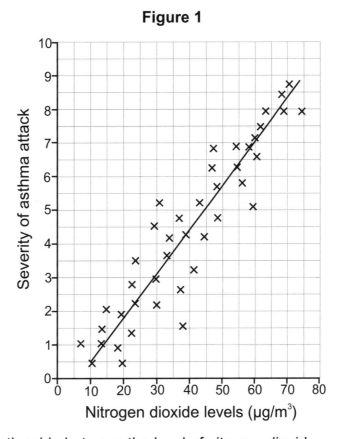

**2.1** Describe the relationship between the level of nitrogen dioxide in the air and the severity of asthma attacks shown in **Figure 1**.

......................................................................................................................................

......................................................................................................................................

*[1 mark]*

**2.2** The scientists decided they could not draw a general conclusion about the link between nitrogen dioxide levels and the severity of asthma attacks that would apply to everyone.
Which of these reasons **does not** describe why this might be the case? Tick **one** box.

☐ The scientists would need to collect data from women too.

☐ The severity of asthma attacks might be affected by another pollutant which happens to be abundant in the same areas as nitrogen dioxide.

☐ The sample of people that the scientists collected data from was too big.

☐ The scientists would need to collect data from other age groups too.

*[1 mark]*

**Question 1 continues on the next page**

**Turn over ▶**

**2.3**   Where do the oxides of nitrogen in the air come from?
Suggest why levels of nitrogen oxides can be particularly high in cities.

.................................................................................................................................

.................................................................................................................................

.................................................................................................................................

.................................................................................................................................

*[3 marks]*


**2.4**   Nitrogen dioxide dissolves in water to form acid rain.
Name **one** other pollutant gas that can cause acid rain.

.................................................................................................................................

*[1 mark]*

**3**    In the UK, the majority of our drinking water is produced from treating groundwater or surface water.  Drinking water can also be made by treating sea water or waste water.

**3.1**  Producing water that is safe to drink from sea water is expensive.
Suggest why some countries produce drinking water by this method.

.......................................................................................................................................................
                                                                                                                    *[1 mark]*

**3.2**  What is the name of the process used to remove salt from sea water?
Tick **one** box

☐  Filtration

☐  Desalination

☐  Sterilisation

☐  Cracking
                                                                                                                    *[1 mark]*

**3.3**  A teacher gives a student a sample of sea water,
and asks her to produce a sample of pure water from it.
Outline a method that the student could use to remove the salt from the sea water.

.......................................................................................................................................................

.......................................................................................................................................................

.......................................................................................................................................................

.......................................................................................................................................................

.......................................................................................................................................................

.......................................................................................................................................................

.......................................................................................................................................................

.......................................................................................................................................................

.......................................................................................................................................................

.......................................................................................................................................................

.......................................................................................................................................................
                                                                                                                    *[6 marks]*

**Question 3 continues on the next page**

**Turn over ▶**

**3.4**   Sewage treatment plants process sewage and release clean, treated water back into the environment.  The first step in the treatment of sewage is screening.
What happens in the screening step?
Tick **one** box.

☐ Chlorine is added to the sewage to kill microorganisms.

☐ The sewage is placed into large storage tanks and allowed to settle.

☐ Anaerobic digestion is used to break down the sewage.

☐ Large bits of material (such as grit) are removed from the sewage.

*[1 mark]*

**3.5**   Following screening, sedimentation is used to separate the effluent from the sludge.
Describe what happens to the effluent before it can be returned to the environment.

......................................................................................................................................

......................................................................................................................................

......................................................................................................................................

*[2 marks]*

4    This question is about the evolution of the atmosphere.

The pie charts in **Figure 2** show the composition of Earth's atmosphere as it may have been 4 billion years ago and as it is at the present time.

**Figure 2**

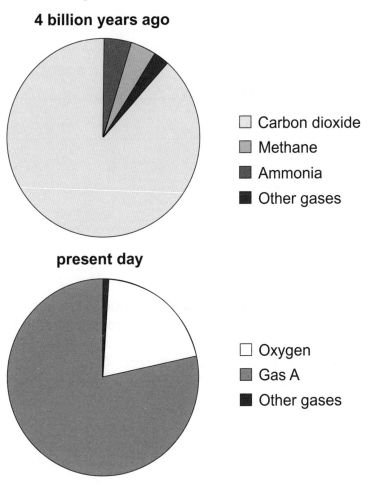

**4 billion years ago**

☐ Carbon dioxide
▨ Methane
▧ Ammonia
■ Other gases

**present day**

☐ Oxygen
▨ Gas A
■ Other gases

4.1    Name Gas A.

.......................................................................................................................................

*[1 mark]*

4.2    The evolution of algae and plants affected the composition of gases in the atmosphere. Explain how algae and plants changed the atmosphere.

.......................................................................................................................................

.......................................................................................................................................

.......................................................................................................................................

.......................................................................................................................................

*[3 marks]*

**Question 4 continues on the next page**

**Turn over ▶**

**4.3**   Human activity is affecting the composition of the atmosphere.
Suggest **one** reason why each of the following factors affects
the level of carbon dioxide in the atmosphere.

Deforestation ...................................................................................................................

........................................................................................................................................

Increased energy consumption ..........................................................................................

........................................................................................................................................

Increasing population ........................................................................................................

........................................................................................................................................

*[3 marks]*

**4.4**   A student says:

"I think that if the amount of carbon dioxide in the atmosphere continues to rise,
this may lead to a drop in global food production in the future."

Explain why the student may be correct.

........................................................................................................................................

........................................................................................................................................

........................................................................................................................................

........................................................................................................................................

........................................................................................................................................

........................................................................................................................................

*[3 marks]*

**5**     A student is investigating how the rate of the reaction between calcium carbonate
and hydrochloric acid is affected by the concentration of the acid.

The student uses the following method:

- Weigh out 10 g of calcium carbonate.
- Add the calcium carbonate to an excess of 7.3 g/dm³ hydrochloric acid
  in a conical flask.
- Use a gas syringe to collect the gas given off by the reaction.
- Measure and record the volume of gas produced every 10 s.
- Repeat the experiment using hydrochloric acid with a concentration of 14.6 g/dm³.

**5.1**   Suggest **two** variables other than the mass of calcium carbonate that the
student would have to keep the same for each run to make it a fair test.

...................................................................................................................................................

...................................................................................................................................................

*[2 marks]*

**Figure 3** shows the student's results for the first
experiment, using 7.3 g/dm³ hydrochloric acid.

**Figure 3**

**Question 5 continues on the next page**

**Turn over ▶**

**5.2** Draw a tangent to the graph in **Figure 3** at 50 seconds.
Using the gradient of the tangent, find the rate of the reaction at this time.
Include the units of the rate in your answer.

...........................................................................................................................................

...........................................................................................................................................

...........................................................................................................................................

...........................................................................................................................................

...........................................................................................................................................

Rate of reaction = ........................................ Unit = ...........................

*[4 marks]*

The first student added the results of his second experiment, using 14.6 g/dm³ hydrochloric acid, to his graph.
This graph is shown in **Figure 4**, below.

**Figure 4**

**5.3** Explain how the student could tell from his graph that increasing the concentration of the acid had increased the reaction rate.

.......................................................................................................................................................

.......................................................................................................................................................
*[1 mark]*

**5.4** In terms of collision theory, explain why concentration affects the rate of a reaction.

.......................................................................................................................................................

.......................................................................................................................................................

.......................................................................................................................................................

.......................................................................................................................................................
*[2 marks]*

**Question 5 continues on the next page**

**Turn over ▶**

A second student is investigating the properties of vinegar. Ethanoic acid is found in vinegar. The student reacted some vinegar with solid sodium carbonate.
The apparatus that he used is shown in **Figure 5**.

**Figure 5**

The student recorded the initial mass of the flask and then recorded it again after 60 s.
He repeated the experiment three times. His results are shown in **Table 2**.

**Table 2**

|  | Initial Mass in g | Final Mass in g | Loss of Mass in g |
|---|---|---|---|
| Run 1 | 128.00 | 127.61 | 0.39 |
| Run 2 | 128.50 | 127.95 | 0.55 |
| Run 3 | 128.35 | 127.90 | 0.45 |

5.5 Calculate the mean loss of mass after 60 s.

......................................................................................................................................................

mean mass lost = ..................... g

*[2 marks]*

5.6 The student repeats the experiment a fourth time, but this time
he collects the gas released by the reaction in a gas syringe.
Name the gas that the student collects.
Describe a test that he could use to confirm the identity of the gas.

......................................................................................................................................................

......................................................................................................................................................

......................................................................................................................................................

*[3 marks]*

**6** The extraction and use of metals in modern life can have a damaging effect on the environment.

The extraction of aluminium from ores requires the electrolysis of aluminium oxide. **Table 3** shows the average energy consumption per kilogram of aluminium produced by the electrolysis of aluminium oxide and recycling.

**Table 3**

|  | Average energy consumption (kWh/kg) |
|---|---|
| Extraction using electrolysis | 15 |
| Recycling | 0.75 |

**6.1** Using the information in **Table 3** and your own knowledge, discuss why it is more sustainable to recycle, where possible, than to mine and extract new metals.

...........................................................................................................................................

...........................................................................................................................................

...........................................................................................................................................

...........................................................................................................................................

...........................................................................................................................................

...........................................................................................................................................

...........................................................................................................................................

...........................................................................................................................................

...........................................................................................................................................

...........................................................................................................................................

...........................................................................................................................................

...........................................................................................................................................

...........................................................................................................................................

...........................................................................................................................................

...........................................................................................................................................

*[6 marks]*

**Question 6 continues on the next page**

**Turn over ▶**

**6.2** Copper, like aluminium, can be extracted from ores using a process that requires a large amount of electricity. However, a lower energy alternative called phytomining can be used to extract copper from low-grade ores. Describe how copper is extracted from low-grade ores using phytomining.

.......................................................................................................................................................

.......................................................................................................................................................

.......................................................................................................................................................

.......................................................................................................................................................

.......................................................................................................................................................

*[4 marks]*

**7** A company uses a process called the contact process to make sulfuric acid.
The first step of the process is the exothermic reaction of sulfur dioxide and oxygen to form sulfur trioxide. The equation for the reaction is shown below.

$$2SO_{2(g)} + O_{2(g)} \rightleftharpoons 2SO_{3(g)}$$

**7.1** This reaction can reach equilibrium.
When a reaction is at equilibrium, what does this tell you about the forward and reverse reactions?

....................................................................................................................................

....................................................................................................................................
*[1 mark]*

**7.2** You can predict how changing the conditions will affect this reaction using Le Chatelier's principle.
What is Le Chatelier's principle?

....................................................................................................................................

....................................................................................................................................
*[1 mark]*

**7.3** State what will happen to the yield of sulfur trioxide in this reaction if the pressure inside the reaction vessel is increased.
Explain your answer.

....................................................................................................................................

....................................................................................................................................

....................................................................................................................................

....................................................................................................................................
*[3 marks]*

**Question 7 continues on the next page**

**Turn over ▶**

184

**7.4** A measured mass of vanadium oxide was added to the reaction vessel at the start of the process. The same mass of vanadium oxide is present at the end of the reaction. Suggest what role vanadium oxide is playing in this reaction.

.............................................................................................................................................

*[1 mark]*

**7.5** The company used to produce 7500 kg of sulfur trioxide each day.
After modifying the plant to allow the sulfur trioxide to be removed from the reaction vessel as soon as it is made, the yield of the plant increased by 15%.
How much sulfur trioxide can the plant make in five days now?

.............................................................................................................................................

.............................................................................................................................................

.............................................................................................................................................

mass made in five days = ........................... kg

*[3 marks]*

**END OF QUESTIONS**

## Topic 1 — Atomic Structure and the Periodic Table

### Pages 22-23

#### Warm-Up Questions

1) The total number of protons and neutrons.
2) An element is a substance that consists of only one type of atom.
3) A compound is a substance made from two or more elements in fixed proportions throughout the compound and they're held together by chemical bonds.
4) ions
5) $C_6H_{12}O_6 + 6O_2 \rightarrow 6CO_2 + 6H_2O$

#### Exam Questions

1.1

| Name of particle | Relative charge |
|------------------|-----------------|
| Proton | **+1** |
| Neutron | **0** |

*[2 marks — 1 mark for each correct charge]*

1.2 nucleus *[1 mark]*
1.3 8 *[1 mark]*
1.4 1 *[1 mark]*
2.1 7 *[1 mark]*
2.2 The number of protons is the same as the atomic number *[1 mark]*
2.3 N *[1 mark]*
3.1 methane and oxygen *[1 mark]*
3.2 carbon dioxide and water *[1 mark]*
3.3 oxygen/$O_2$ *[1 mark]*
3.4 $CH_4 + \mathbf{2O_2} \rightarrow CO_2 + \mathbf{2H_2O}$
*[1 mark for correct missing reactant, 1 mark for correctly balancing the equation]*
4.1 $\mathbf{H_2SO_4} + \mathbf{2NH_3} \rightarrow \mathbf{(NH_4)_2SO_4}$ *[1 mark for each correct reactant, 1 mark for correctly balancing the equation]*
4.2 15 *[1 mark]*
*There are eight atoms of hydrogen, one atom of sulfur, four atoms of oxygen, and two atoms of nitrogen.*
4.3 8
*There are 4 hydrogen atoms in $NH_4$ and there are two of these.*
5.1 An isotope is a different atomic form of the same element *[1 mark]*, which has the same number of protons *[1 mark]* but a different number of neutrons *[1 mark]*.
5.2 Protons = 6 *[1 mark]*, neutrons = 7 *[1 mark]*, electrons = 6 *[1 mark]*
5.3 It has a different atomic number from carbon *[1 mark]*.
5.4 $(79 \times 13) + (21 \times 14) = 1321$
Relative atomic mass = $1321 \div 100 = 13.21 = \mathbf{13.2}$
*[4 marks for correct final answer, otherwise give 1 mark for each correct stage of working]*

### Page 30

#### Warm-Up Questions

1) Two or more elements or compounds mixed together.
2) evaporation / crystallisation
3) fractional distillation

#### Exam Questions

1.1 E.g. put the paper in a beaker of solvent, e.g. water *[1 mark]*.
1.2 Pencil marks are insoluble (so won't dissolve into the solvent) *[1 mark]*.
2.1 E.g. mix the lawn sand with water to dissolve the ammonium sulfate *[1 mark]*. Filter the mixture using filter paper to remove the sharp sand *[1 mark]*. Pour the remaining solution into an evaporating dish and slowly heat it to evaporate the water until you have a dry product *[1 mark]*.
2.2 E.g. the products were not completely dry *[1 mark]*.
3.1 The boiling points of water and methanoic acid are too close together to allow them to be separated by simple distillation *[1 mark]*.

3.2

| Temperature on thermometer | Contents of the flask | Contents of the beaker |
|----------------------------|----------------------|------------------------|
| 30 °C | both liquids | no liquid |
| 65 °C | water | propanone |
| 110 °C | no liquid | both liquids |

*[3 marks for whole table correct otherwise 1 mark for each correct row]*

### Page 36

#### Warm-Up Questions

1) The 'plum pudding model' — a ball of positive charge with electrons stuck in it.
2) a) 2
   b) 8
3) The discovery of isotopes.

#### Exam Questions

1.1

*[1 mark]*
1.2 Any one of: lithium / potassium / rubidium / caesium / francium *[1 mark]*
1.3 1 *[1 mark]*
2.1 By atomic mass *[1 mark]*
2.2 By atomic number *[1 mark]*
2.3 Similar chemical properties due to having the same number of electrons in their outer shell *[1 mark]*.
3 How to grade your answer:
Level 0: No description is given. *[No marks]*
Level 1: Brief description of how the theory of atomic structure has changed. *[1 to 2 marks]*
Level 2: Some detail given of how the theory of atomic structure has changed. *[3 to 4 marks]*
Level 3: A clear and detailed description of how the theory of atomic structure has changed. *[5 to 6 marks]*
Here are some points your answer may include:
At the start of the 19th century John Dalton described atoms as solid spheres that make up the different elements.
In 1897 JJ Thomson concluded that atoms weren't solid spheres and that an atom must contain smaller, negatively charged particles (electrons). He called this the 'plum pudding model'.
In 1909 Ernest Rutherford conducted a gold foil experiment, firing positively charged particles at an extremely thin sheet of gold. Most of the particles went straight through, so he concluded that there was a positively charged nucleus at the centre, surrounded by a 'cloud' of negative electrons.
Niels Bohr proposed a new model of the atom where all the electrons were contained in shells. He suggested that electrons can only exist in fixed orbits, or shells.
Further experimentation by Rutherford and others showed that the nucleus could be divided into smaller particles, each with the same charge as a hydrogen atom, these became known as protons.
James Chadwick carried out an experiment which provided evidence of the existence of neutral particles within the nucleus, which became known as neutrons.

### Pages 43-44

#### Warm-Up Questions

1) positive ions
2) Any three of: e.g. strong / can be bent or hammered into different shapes / conduct heat / conduct electricity / high melting point / high boiling point.
3) lithium oxide / $Li_2O$
4) negative
5) Group 0

## Exam Questions

1.1 Highest (X): fluorine *[1 mark]*. Lowest (Y): iodine *[1 mark]*.
1.2 iodine *[1 mark]*
2.1 alkali metals/Group 1 elements *[1 mark]*
2.2 To the right of the line *[1 mark]*. Since it does not conduct electricity, it must be a non-metal *[1 mark]*.
3.1 ionic bonds *[1 mark]*
3.2 E.g. displacement reaction *[1 mark]*
3.3 iodine/$I_2$ *[1 mark]* as it is displaced from potassium iodide *[1 mark]*.
3.4 The products of the reaction will be aqueous potassium chloride/$KCl_{(aq)}$ *[1 mark]* and bromine gas/$Br_{2(g)}$ *[1 mark]*. Chlorine is more reactive than bromine as its outer shell is closer to the nucleus *[1 mark]*. This results in chlorine displacing bromine from potassium bromide *[1 mark]*.
3.5 Group 0 elements are generally inert *[1 mark]*. This is because they are energetically stable and don't need to lose or gain electrons to have a full outer shell *[1 mark]*.
4.1 They have a single outer electron which is easily lost so they are very reactive *[1 mark]*.
4.2 As you go down Group 1, the outer electron is further from the nucleus *[1 mark]*. So the attraction between the nucleus and the electron decreases *[1 mark]*. This means the outer electron is more easily lost and the metal is more reactive *[1 mark]*.
4.3 hydrogen *[1 mark]* and potassium hydroxide *[1 mark]*
4.4 alkaline *[1 mark]*

# Topic 2 — Bonding, Structure and Properties of Matter

## Page 51
### Warm-Up Questions
1) A charged atom or group of atoms.
2) +2
3) −1
4) high
5) When ionic compounds dissolve in water, the ions separate and are all free to move in the solution, so they'll carry an electric current.
6) $Al(OH)_3$

### Exam Questions
1.1 Sodium will lose the electron from its outer shell to form a positive ion *[1 mark]*. Fluorine will gain an electron to form a negative ion *[1 mark]*.
1.2 Ionic compounds have a giant ionic lattice structure *[1 mark]*. The ions form a closely packed regular lattice arrangement *[1 mark]*, held together by strong electrostatic forces of attraction between oppositely charged ions *[1 mark]*.
2.1 lithium oxide *[1 mark]*
2.2

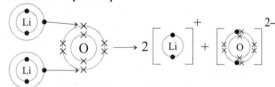

*[1 mark for arrows shown correctly, 1 mark for correct electron arrangement and charge on lithium ion, 1 mark for correct electron arrangement and charge on oxygen ion]*
2.3 When molten, the $Li^+$ and $O^{2-}$ ions are able to move *[1 mark]*. These ions are able to carry electric current *[1 mark]*.
2.4 The formula of the compound is **LiCl** *[1 mark]*. Lithium is in Group 1, so forms +1 ions. Chlorine is in Group 7, so forms −1 ions. Therefore there needs to be one lithium ion for every chlorine ion for the compound to be neutral *[1 mark]*.

## Page 55
### Warm-Up Questions
1) A chemical bond made by the sharing of a pair of electrons between two atoms.
2) 3
3) gas or liquid
4) covalent bonds
5) intermolecular forces

### Exam Questions
1

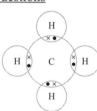

*[1 mark for showing a pairs of shared electrons between C and H, 1 mark for no other electrons shown]*
2.1

*[1 mark for showing 2 pairs of shared electrons between O atoms, 1 mark for showing two non-bonding pairs of electrons on each oxygen]*
2.2 3 *[1 mark]*
3.1 Hydrogen chloride doesn't contain any ions or delocalised electrons to carry a charge *[1 mark]*.
3.2 E.g. a pair of electrons (one from the hydrogen atom and one from the chlorine atom) is shared between the two atoms *[1 mark]*. The atoms are held together by the strong attraction between this shared pair of negatively charged electrons and the positively charged nuclei of the atoms *[1 mark]*.
3.3 Chlorine is a larger molecule than hydrogen chloride *[1 mark]* and therefore there are greater intermolecular forces between molecules *[1 mark]*. As the intermolecular forces are greater between chlorine molecules, its boiling point is higher than hydrogen chloride *[1 mark]*.

*Chlorine has three shells of electrons, whereas hydrogen only has one. So $Cl_2$ is a bigger molecule than HCl.*

## Page 61
### Warm-Up Questions
1) By covalent bonding.
2) solid
3) E.g. diamond is much harder than graphite. Diamond doesn't conduct electricity whereas graphite does.
4) Buckminsterfullerene
5) The layers of atom in metals are able to slide over each other.

### Exam Questions
1.1 In a giant covalent structure, all of the atoms are bonded to each other with strong covalent bonds *[1 mark]*. It takes lots of energy to break these bonds and melt the solid *[1 mark]*.
1.2 E.g. diamond / graphite / silicon dioxide *[1 mark]*
2.1 Graphite is formed of layers of carbon atoms that are held together weakly *[1 mark]*. The layers can easily slide over each other, making graphite soft and slippery *[1 mark]*.
2.2 In diamond, each carbon atom forms four covalent bonds in a very rigid structure *[1 mark]*. This makes diamond very hard, so it would be good at cutting other substances *[1 mark]*.
2.3 Any one from: e.g. delivering drugs / catalysts / lubricants / strengthening materials *[1 mark]*
2.4 E.g. each carbon atom has a delocalised electron that is able to carry the charge *[1 mark]*.

3.1 E.g.

*[1 mark for showing two different sizes of atoms, 1 mark for showing irregular arrangement]*

3.2 The regular arrangement of atoms in iron means that they can slide over each other, resulting in iron being soft *[1 mark]*. Steel contains different sized atoms which distort the layers of iron atoms *[1 mark]* making it more difficult for them to slide over each other *[1 mark]*.

## Page 65
### Warm-Up Questions
1) The material, the temperature and the pressure.
2) solid
3) weak
4) The particles move faster.
5) Lots of bonds have formed between gas particles so the gas becomes a liquid.
6) $Na^+_{(aq)}$

### Exam Questions
1.1 In solids, there are **strong** *[1 mark]* forces of attraction between particles, which hold them in fixed positions in a **regular** *[1 mark]* arrangement. The particles don't **move** *[1 mark]* from their positions, so solids keep their shape. The **hotter** *[1 mark]* the solid becomes, the more the particles in the solid vibrate.
1.2 The particles gain energy, so they move faster *[1 mark]*. The intermolecular bonds are weakened and, when they have enough energy, they break *[1 mark]*. This means the particles are free to move far apart from each other and the liquid becomes a gas *[1 mark]*.
2.1 The particles are free to move about / have virtually no forces of attraction between them *[1 mark]*, so they move randomly, spreading out to fill the container *[1 mark]*.
2.2 There's a weak force of attraction between the particles in a liquid *[1 mark]*. This means they're free to move past each other but tend to stick closely together *[1 mark]*.
2.3 gas *[1 mark]*

## Topic 3 — Quantitative Chemistry
### Page 71
### Warm-Up Questions
1) relative formula mass
2) Avogadro constant
3) A mole is an amount of a substance that contains as many particles as the Avogadro constant ($6.02 \times 10^{23}$).
4) 56
5) One mole of $O_2$ weighs $16 \times 2 = $ **32 g**

### Exam Questions
1.1 $M_r$ of $BF_3 = 11 + (19 \times 3) = $ **68** *[1 mark]*
1.2 $M_r$ of $B(OH)_3 = 11 + (17 \times 3) = $ **62** *[1 mark]*
2 number of moles $= \dfrac{\text{mass in grams}}{M_r}$ *[1 mark]*
3 $M_r$ of KOH $= (39 + 16 + 1) = $ **56** *[1 mark]*
Mass of 4 moles of KOH $= 4 \times 56 = $ **224 g** *[1 mark]*
Extra mass needed $= 224 - 140 = $ **84 g** *[1 mark]*
4.1 Oxygen in the air, which previously couldn't be weighed, has now reacted with metal **X** to form a solid oxide *[1 mark]*.
4.2 $100 - 40 = $ **60%** *[1 mark]*
4.3 Mass of metal **X** in 8.0 g of mixture:
$= 8.0 \times (24 \div 100) = $ **1.92 g** *[1 mark]*

The metal oxide contains 60% metal **X** by mass, so the mass of metal oxide used to make the mixture $= 1.92 \div (60 \div 100) = $ **3.2 g** *[1 mark]*.

## Page 75
### Warm-Up Questions
1) The number of moles of each substance taking part in or made by the reaction.
2) To make sure that all of the other reactant reacts.
3) It halves.
4) The amount of a substance in a certain volume of a solution.

### Exam Questions
1.1 Li: $3.5 \div 7 = $ **0.5 mol**
$O_2$: $4.0 \div 32 = $ **0.125 mol**
$Li_2O$: $7.5 \div 30 = $ **0.25 mol**
*[2 marks for all three correct answers, otherwise 1 mark for two correct answers]*
1.2 Divide by the smallest number of moles (0.125):
Li: $\frac{0.5}{0.125} = 4$   $H_2$: $\frac{0.125}{0.125} = 1$   $Li_2O$: $\frac{0.25}{0.125} = 2$ *[1 mark]*
The balanced symbol equation is:
$4Li + O_2 \rightarrow 2Li_2O$ *[1 mark]*
2.1 $M_r$ of $NaHCO_3 = 23 + 1 + 12 + (3 \times 16) = 84$ *[1 mark]*
no. of moles of $NaHCO_3 = 6.0 \div 84 = 0.0714...$ mol *[1 mark]*
1 mole of $Na_2SO_4$ is made for every 2 moles of $NaHCO_3$ that reacts, so no. of moles of $Na_2SO_4 = 0.0714... \div 2 = 0.0357...$ mol *[1 mark]*
$M_r$ of $Na_2SO_4 = (2 \times 23) + 32 + (4 \times 16) = 142$ *[1 mark]*
Mass of $Na_2SO_4 = 142 \times 0.0357... = 5.071... = $ **5.1 g (2 s.f.)** *[1 mark]*
2.2 The limiting reactant is the reactant that gets used up and therefore limits the amount of product formed *[1 mark]*.
3.1 $160 \div 1000 = 0.160$ $dm^3$ *[1 mark]*
concentration = mass ÷ volume
$= 24.5 \div 0.160 = $ **153.125 g/dm** *[1 mark]*
$= $ **153 g/dm³** (to 3 s.f.) *[1 mark]*
3.2 $200 \div 1000 = 0.20$ $dm^3$ *[1 mark]*
mass = concentration × volume $= 75 \times 0.2 = $ **15 g** *[1 mark]*
3.3 640 g = 0.640 kg *[1 mark]*
concentration = 56 kg per 100 $dm^3$ = 0.56 kg/$dm^3$ *[1 mark]*
volume = mass ÷ concentration = $0.640 \div 0.56$
$= $ **1.14285... dm³** *[1 mark]*
$= $ **1.14 dm³** (3 s.f.) *[1 mark]*

## Topic 4 — Chemical Changes
### Page 81
### Warm-Up Questions
1) 0-14
2) neutral
3) Strong acids ionise completely in water, so all of the acid particles dissociate to release $H^+$ ions. Weak acids do not fully ionise, so only some of the acid particles dissociate to release $H^+$ ions.
4) Difference in pH $= 5 - 2 = 3$
Factor $H^+$ ion concentration changes by $= 10^{-3} = 0.001$
*You could give your answer here as '$10^{-3}$', '0.001' or 'it decreased by a factor of 1000' — they all mean the same thing.*
5) Copper nitrate and water.

### Exam Questions
1.1 $H^+$ ions/hydrogen ions *[1 mark]*
1.2 neutralisation *[1 mark]*
2.1 alkalis *[1 mark]*
2.2 $2HNO_3 + Mg(OH)_2 \rightarrow Mg(NO_3)_2 + 2H_2O$
*[1 mark for formulas of both products correct, 1 mark for putting a 2 in front of $H_2O$ to balance the equation]*
3.1 E.g. the excess silver carbonate will sink to the bottom of the flask and stay there / the mixture will stop producing bubbles (of carbon dioxide) *[1 mark]*.
3.2 filtration *[1 mark]*
3.3 Heat the silver nitrate solution gently using a water bath/electric heater to evaporate some of the water *[1 mark]*. Leave the solution to cool until crystals form *[1 mark]*. Filter out the crystals and dry them *[1 mark]*.

Page 87

Warm-Up Questions

1)      How easily it loses electrons to form positive ions.
2)      magnesium chloride
3)      A metal hydroxide and hydrogen.
4) a)   $Zn_{(s)} + Cu^{2+}_{(aq)} \rightarrow Zn^{2+}_{(aq)} + Cu_{(s)}$
   b)   zinc / Zn

Exam Questions

1.1     Any one from: potassium / sodium / calcium *[1 mark]*.
1.2     copper *[1 mark]*
*Metals below hydrogen in the reactivity series don't react with acids.*
1.3     E.g. iron and dilute acid would produce bubbles
        of hydrogen gas *[1 mark]* more slowly than zinc
        and dilute acid / very slowly *[1 mark]*.
*You don't need to use these exact words — the two points you need to
cover are that it would still produce hydrogen gas, but at a slower rate
than the zinc.*
2.1     $2Fe_2O_3 + 3C \rightarrow 4Fe + 3CO_2$
        *[1 mark for formulas of all reactants and products
        correct, 1 mark for correctly balancing the equation]*
2.2     Oxygen is being lost from iron oxide / the iron(III) ions
        in the iron oxide are gaining electrons *[1 mark]*.
3       In A there will be no charge *[1 mark]*.  In B the solution
        will have changed from blue to green *[1 mark]* and the grey
        metal will be coated in orange metal *[1 mark]*.  Iron is more
        reactive than copper *[1 mark]*.  So in A, the copper cannot
        displace the iron from iron sulfate *[1 mark]*, but in B, the
        iron does displace the copper from copper sulfate *[1 mark]*.

Page 92

Warm-Up Questions

1)      the cathode / negative electrode
2)      zinc and chlorine gas
3)      reduced
4)      hydrogen gas

Exam Questions

1.1     To lower the melting point of the aluminium oxide *[1 mark]*.
1.2     $Al^{3+} + 3e^- \rightarrow Al$ *[1 mark]*
1.3     $2O^{2-} \rightarrow O_2 + 4e^-$ *[1 mark]*
1.4     The oxygen made at the positive electrode reacts
        with the carbon to make carbon dioxide *[1 mark]*
        wearing the electrode away *[1 mark]*.
2.1     hydrogen *[1 mark]*
2.2     $2H^+ + 2e^- \rightarrow H_2$ *[1 mark]*
2.3     chlorine *[1 mark]*
2.4     $2Cl^- \rightarrow Cl_2 + 2e^- / 2Cl^- - 2e^- \rightarrow Cl_2$ *[1 mark]*
2.5     Sodium is more reactive than hydrogen, so the
        sodium ions from the sodium chloride stay in solution
        *[1 mark]*.  Hydroxide ions are also left in solution
        when hydrogen is produced from water *[1 mark]*.
2.6     Copper is less reactive than hydrogen *[1 mark]*.

Topic 5 — Energy Changes

Page 98

Warm-Up Questions

1)      An exothermic reaction is one which
        transfers energy to the surroundings.
2)      An endothermic reaction is one which takes
        in energy from the surroundings.
3)      When bonds are formed.
4)      The activation energy is the minimum amount of energy
        the reactants need to collide with each other and react.

Exam Questions

1       B *[1 mark]*
2.1     Exothermic, because the temperature of the mixture
        has increased *[1 mark]*, therefore the particles have
        transferred energy to the reaction mixture *[1 mark]*.
2.2     A lid was placed on the cup to reduce energy lost
        to the surroundings (by evaporation) *[1 mark]*.
3.1     C – H and O = O *[1 mark]*

3.2     $(4 \times 414) + (2 \times 494) = 2644$ kJ/mol
*This is the amount of energy required to break the bonds in $CH_4$ and $2O_2$.*
        $(2 \times 800) + (4 \times 459) = 3436$ kJ/mol
*This is the amount of energy released by forming the bonds in $CO_2$
and $2H_2O$.*
        $2644 - 3436 = $ **–792 kJ/mole** *[3 marks for correct answer,
        otherwise 1 mark for finding the energy needed to break
        the bonds in the reactants, 1 mark for finding the energy
        released by forming bonds in the products.]*

Topic 6 — The Rate and Extent
of Chemical Change

Pages 108-109

Warm-Up Questions

1)      E.g. the rusting of iron is a reaction that happens
        very slowly.  Explosions are very fast reactions.
2)      They must collide with enough energy.
3)      There will be more particles in the same volume,
        which will lead to more frequent collisions,
        so the rate of reaction will increase.
4)      g/s
5)      E.g. observe a mark through the solution
        in which the precipitate forms and measure
        how long it takes for it to disappear.

Exam Questions

1.1     stopwatch/stopclock/timer *[1 mark]*
1.2     gas syringe *[1 mark]*
1.3     E.g. place a conical flask on a mass balance
        *[1 mark]* and record the change in mass at regular
        intervals as the gas leaves the flask *[1 mark]*.
2.1     Any two from: e.g. the concentration of sodium thiosulfate/
        hydrochloric acid / the depth of liquid / the person judging
        when the black cross is obscured / the black cross used (size,
        darkness etc.).  *[2 marks — 1 mark for each correct answer.]*
*Judging when a cross is completely obscured is quite subjective — two
people might not agree on exactly when it happens. You can try to limit
this problem by using the same person each time, but you can't remove the
problem completely. The person might have changed their mind slightly by
the time they do the next experiment — or be looking at it from a different
angle, be a bit more bored, etc.*
2.2
        *[1 mark for correctly drawn axes with a sensible scale,
        2 marks for all points plotted correctly, otherwise 1 mark if
        5 of 6 points plotted correctly, 1 mark for a suitable line of
        best fit]*
2.3     As the temperature decreases the time
        decreases, meaning that the reaction is slower
        as the temperature decreases *[1 mark]*.
2.4     At each temperature it would take longer for
        the reaction to complete *[1 mark]*.
2.5     A lower concentration of reactant means there are fewer
        particles in the same volume of solution *[1 mark]*.  This
        makes collisions between the reactant particles less frequent
        *[1 mark]*, and therefore decreases the rate of reaction
        *[1 mark]*.
2.6     E.g. by repeating the experiment *[1 mark]*.  If the results
        gained are similar then the experiment is repeatable *[1 mark]*.
3.1     A *[1 mark]*

3.2

Curve C, as above. The curve should be between curves A and B *[1 mark]*.

3.3 The variables are controlled so that you can tell if the variable you're changing/the dependent variable is causing the results seen *[1 mark]*.

3.4 E.g. yes, because the same volume of gas was produced in each experiment *[1 mark]*.

*This suggests that the same concentration and volume of acid (or an excess of acid) was used in both experiments.*

3.5 Measuring how quickly the reaction loses mass *[1 mark]*.

4.1 Mean rate = amount of product formed ÷ time
= 40 ÷ 60 = **0.67 cm³/s** *[2 marks for correct answer, otherwise 1 mark for correct working]*

4.2 E.g.

*[1 mark for correctly drawn axes with a sensible scale, 2 marks for correctly marking on all 6 points, otherwise 1 mark if 5 of 6 points plotted correctly, 1 mark for a suitable line of best fit.]*

4.3 E.g.

change in $y$ = 40 − 27 = 13, change in $x$ = 38 − 6 = 32,
rate = change in $y$ ÷ change in $x$ = 13 ÷ 32 = **0.4 cm³/s**
*[1 mark for drawing a tangent at 25 s, 1 mark for correctly calculating a change in y from the tangent, 1 mark for correctly calculating a change in x from the tangent and 1 mark for a rate between 0.3 cm/s and 0.5 cm/s]*

5 How to grade your answer:
Level 0: No relevant information is given. *[No marks]*
Level 1: One or two ways of increasing the rate are described and there's reference to collision theory. *[1 to 2 marks]*
Level 2: At least two ways of increasing the rate are given with appropriate reference to collision theory. *[3 to 4 marks]*
Level 3: There is a clear and detailed discussion of three ways by which the rate can be increased, which includes relevant references to collision theory. *[5 to 6 marks]*

Here are some points your answer may include:
Collision theory says that the rate of reaction depends on how often and how hard the reacting particles collide with each other.
If the particles collide hard enough (with enough energy) they will react.
Increasing the temperature makes particles move faster, so they collide more often and with greater energy. This will increase the rate of reaction.
If the surface area of the nickel catalyst is increased then the particles around it will have more area to work on. This increases the frequency of successful collisions and will increase the rate of reaction.
Increasing the pressure of the hydrogen will mean the particles are more squashed up together. This will increase the frequency of the collisions and increase the rate of reaction.

## Page 113
### Warm-Up Questions
1) They are the same.
2) The equilibrium will move to the left/towards reactants and the amount of reactants will increase.
3) It would have no effect (because there are equal numbers of gas molecules on both sides).

### Exam Questions
1.1 The reaction is reversible *[1 mark]*.
1.2 Both (the forward and reverse) reactions are taking place at exactly the same rate *[1 mark]*.
2.1 Less $NO_{2(g)}$ will be produced *[1 mark]*, because there are more molecules of gas on the right hand side of the equation *[1 mark]*.
2.2 It will have no effect *[1 mark]*, because there are the same number of molecules of gas on both sides of the equation *[1 mark]*.
3.1 It gives out energy *[1 mark]*, because it's exothermic *[1 mark]*.

*As the forward reaction is endothermic you know that the reverse reaction is exothermic and therefore gives out energy.*

3.2 A reversible reaction is always exothermic in one direction and endothermic in the other direction *[1 mark]*, so a change in temperature will always favour one reaction more than the other *[1 mark]*.
3.3 It would move to the right *[1 mark]*.

## Topic 7 — Organic Chemistry
### Pages 119-120
### Warm-Up Questions
1) methane, ethane, propane, butane
2) single covalent bonds
3) When burnt they release energy.
4) e.g. fuel for transport / feedstock for making new compounds
5) long-chain hydrocarbons

### Exam Questions
1 ethane *[1 mark]*
2.1 butane *[1 mark]*
2.2 $C_4H_{10}$ *[1 mark]*
2.3 Any two from: e.g. polymers / solvents /lubricants / detergents *[2 marks — 1 mark for each correct answer]*

3

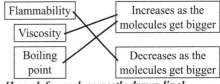

*[1 mark for each correctly drawn line]*

4.1 **F** *[1 mark]*
4.2 **A** *[1 mark]*

4.3     Inside the fractionating column there is a temperature gradient with the hottest part at the bottom and coolest at the top *[1 mark]*. Crude oil that is gaseous moves up the column and when hydrocarbons in the gas reach a part of the column where the temperature is lower than their boiling points they condense and drain out of the column *[1 mark]*. Hydrocarbons with longer chain lengths have higher boiling points so condense lower down the column whereas hydrocarbons with shorter chain lengths have lower boiling points so condense higher up the column *[1 mark]*.

5.1     carbon dioxide/$CO_2$ *[1 mark]* and water/$H_2O$ *[1 mark]*

5.2     $C_3H_8 + 5O_2 \rightarrow 3CO_2 + 4H_2O$ *[1 mark for correct reactants and products, 1 mark for correct balancing]*

5.3     oxidation *[1 mark]*

6.1     Because shorter-chain hydrocarbons generated by cracking tend to be more useful than longer ones *[1 mark]*.

6.2     $C_8H_{18} \rightarrow C_2H_6 + 2C_3H_6$ *[1 mark for correct products, 1 mark for correct balancing]*

6.3     E.g. catalytic cracking is where long-chain hydrocarbons are vaporised *[1 mark]* and then passed over a hot powdered aluminium catalyst *[1 mark]*. Or they can be cracked by steam cracking which is where long-chain hydrocarbons are vaporised and mixed with steam *[1 mark]*. They are then heated to a very high temperature *[1 mark]*.

*You don't have to mention the names of the different cracking methods (catalytic and steam) but it might help structure your answer.*

## Topic 8 — Chemical Analysis
### Page 126
#### Warm-Up Questions
1)     A pure substance is a substance that only contains one compound or one element.
2)     Impurities in a substance will increase the boiling point of the substance and may result in it boiling over a wider temperature range.
3)     E.g. paint / drugs / cleaning products / fuels / cosmetics / fertilisers / metal alloys / food / drink.
4)     Chromatography separates out the substances in a mixture.

#### Exam Questions
1.1     Light the gas with a lighted splint *[1 mark]*. Hydrogen will burn with a squeaky pop *[1 mark]*.

1.2     Place a glowing splint in the sample of gas *[1 mark]*. Oxygen will relight it *[1 mark]*.

2.1     D *[1 mark]*

2.2     A *[1 mark]*

2.3     C *[1 mark]*

2.4     $R_f$ = distance travelled by substance in sunrise yellow ÷ distance travelled by solvent
    $R_f = 9.0 \div 12.0 = 0.75$
    *[2 marks for correct answer, otherwise 1 mark for using the correct formula to calculate $R_f$]*

## Topic 9 — Chemistry of the Atmosphere
### Page 135
#### Warm-Up Questions
1)     volcanic activity
2)     E.g. limestone / coal
3)     E.g. coal / crude oil / natural gas
4)     E.g. walk, cycle, or take public transport instead of using their car for a journey / reduce their use of air travel / turn down their heating at home.
5)     Any two from: e.g. carbon monoxide / soot / unburned hydrocarbons / particulates.

#### Exam Questions
1     Once green plants had evolved, they thrived in Earth's early atmosphere which was rich in **carbon dioxide** *[1 mark]*. These plants also produced **oxygen** *[1 mark]* by the process of **photosynthesis** *[1 mark]*. Some of the **carbon** *[1 mark]* from dead plants eventually became 'locked up' in fossil fuels.

2.1     When sulfur dioxide gas reacts with water in clouds *[1 mark]* it forms dilute sulfuric acid, which falls as rain *[1 mark]*.

2.2     E.g. it kills plants / damages buildings and statues / makes metals corrode *[1 mark]*.

2.3     Incomplete combustion of fossil fuels produces particulates *[1 mark]*. Particulates (and the clouds they help to produce) reflect sunlight back into space *[1 mark]* so less light reaches the Earth *[1 mark]*.

2.4     Short wavelength radiation from the sun passes through the Earth's atmosphere *[1 mark]*. It hits the Earth's surface and is reflected back as long wavelength radiation *[1 mark]*. This long wavelength radiation is absorbed by greenhouse gases in the atmosphere *[1 mark]*. They re-radiate it in all directions, including back towards the Earth, warming its surface *[1 mark]*.

3.1     A measure of the amount of carbon dioxide and other greenhouse gases released over the full life-cycle of a product, service or event *[1 mark]*.

3.2     How to grade your answer:
    Level 0:   There is no relevant information. *[No marks]*
    Level 1:   There is a brief description of at least one potential effect of an increase in global temperature. Some attempt is made to explain what impact this effect could have on humans. *[1 to 2 marks]*
    Level 2:   There is some description of at least two potential effects of an increase in global temperature and an explanation of the potential impact of these effects on humans. *[3 to 4 marks]*
    Level 3:   There is a clear and detailed explanation of at least three effects of an increase in global temperature and a clear explanation of the potential impact of these effects on humans. *[5 to 6 marks]*

Here are some points your answer may include:

Effect: An increase in global temperature could lead to polar ice caps melting. This could cause a rise in sea levels.

Impacts: Rising seas levels could cause flooding in coastal areas and cause coastal erosion.

Flooding and coastal erosion could make people who live near the coast homeless / cause costly damage to buildings and roads / pose a threat to human life.

Effect: Climate change could lead to changes in rainfall patterns.

Impacts: Some regions may have too much or too little water. Having too little water may affect the ability of certain regions to produce enough food for the human population. This could lead to famine or even starvation. Too much water could lead to flooding.

Flooding could make people homeless / cause costly damage to buildings and roads / pose a threat to human life.

Effect: Climate change may lead to an increase in both the frequency and severity of storms.

Impacts: Storms can cause damage to buildings and roads and can pose a direct threat to human life.

Effect: Rising temperatures can directly affect the human and wildlife populations in an area.

Impacts: An increase in temperature may affect what food plants can be grown in a certain region. This could lead to famine or even starvation.

## Topic 10 — Using Resources
### Page 142
#### Warm-Up Questions
1)     E.g. natural rubber
2)     Development that takes account of the needs of present society while not damaging the lives of future generations.
3)     E.g. saves energy needed to extract metals from the earth / conserves limited supplies of metals from the earth / cuts down on the amount of waste going to landfill.
4)     E.g. getting the raw materials / manufacturing and packaging / using the product / product disposal.

## Exam Questions

1.1 A natural resource that doesn't renew itself quick enough to be considered replaceable *[1 mark]*.

1.2 Any two from: e.g. reuse the cans / recycle the aluminium / use fewer cans *[2 marks]*.

2.1 E.g. because the supply of copper-rich ores is limited *[1 mark]*.

2.2 Bacteria convert copper compounds in the ore into soluble copper compounds which separate out from the ore *[1 mark]*. This produces a (leachate) solution containing copper ions, from which copper can be extracted by electrolysis/ displacement with a more reactive metal e.g. scrap iron *[1 mark]*.

2.3 E.g. these processes have a smaller environmental impact *[1 mark]*.

2.4 E.g. these processes are slower *[1 mark]*.

3.1 The effect of some pollutants produced in the life cycle of a product can be difficult to quantify *[1 mark]*.

3.2 E.g. the person carrying out the company's LCA may have purposely not included details of the disposal of the product *[1 mark]*, because the company wanted to use the LCA to support that their product was environmentally friendly for advertising reasons *[1 mark]*.

## Page 146

### Warm-Up Questions

1) Any two from: e.g. the levels of dissolved salts in the water aren't too high / the water has a pH of between 6.5 and 8.5 / there aren't any bacteria or other microbes in the water.

2) filtration

3) harmful chemicals

4) effluent and sludge

### Exam Questions

1.1 Potable water contains dissolved substances whereas pure water only contains water molecules *[1 mark]*.

1.2 First, large bits of material are removed by a wire mesh *[1 mark]*, then sand and gravel beds filter out any other solid bits *[1 mark]*.

1.3 E.g. chlorine / ozone / ultraviolet light *[1 mark for each correct answer up to a maximum of three marks.]*

2.1 screening *[1 mark]*

2.2 The effluent undergoes aerobic digestion *[1 mark]*. During aerobic digestion air is pumped through the effluent which encourages aerobic bacteria to break down any organic matter in the water *[1 mark]*.

2.3 E.g. processes used to treat waste and sea water use more energy than treating fresh water and are therefore more expensive *[1 mark]*. People may not like the idea of drinking treated waste water *[1 mark]*.

3.1 E.g. sodium ions can be tested for by carrying out a flame test using a sample of water *[1 mark]*. If sodium ions are present the flame will turn yellow *[1 mark]*. To test for chloride ions a few drops of dilute nitric acid should be added to a sample of water, followed by a few drops of silver nitrate solution *[1 mark]*. If chloride ions are present, a white precipitate will form *[1 mark]*.

3.2 E.g. the pH of the water would need to be tested to see if it is between 6.5 and 8.5 *[1 mark]*.

## Practice Paper 1

### Pages 154-167

1.1 +1 *[1 mark]*

1.2 Any two from: e.g. potassium fizzes more than sodium, which fizzes more than lithium / potassium moves more quickly than sodium, which moves more quickly than lithium / potassium melts and a flame is seen, sodium melts but no flame is seen and lithium does not melt *[1 mark for each correct observation]*.

1.3 As you go down Group 1 the outer electron gets further from the nucleus *[1 mark]*. This means that the outer electron is more easily lost because it feels less attraction from the nucleus *[1 mark]*. So reactivity increases as you go down Group 1/from lithium to sodium to potassium *[1 mark]*.

1.4 $2Li + 2H_2O \rightarrow 2LiOH + H_2$
*[1 mark for formulas of both products correct, 1 mark for correct balancing]*

1.5 It contains hydroxide ions *[1 mark]*.

1.6 Protons = 9 *[1 mark]*
Neutrons = 19 − 9 = 10 *[1 mark]*
Electrons = 9 *[1 mark]*
*Remember: number of protons = atomic number, number of neutrons = mass number − atomic number, number of electrons (in a neutral atom) = number of protons.*

2.1

*[1 mark for adding seven crosses and one dot to outer shell of Cl⁻ ion, 1 mark for correct charge on both ions.]*

2.2 The molecules in substance A are only attracted to each other by weak intermolecular forces *[1 mark]* which don't need much energy to break/overcome *[1 mark]*.

2.3 Substance C *[1 mark]*. It has a high melting and boiling point and can conduct electricity when molten or dissolved but not when solid *[1 mark]*.

2.4 How to grade your answer:

Level 0: There is no relevant information. *[No marks]*

Level 1: A brief attempt is made to explain one or two of these properties in terms of structure and bonding. *[1 to 2 marks]*

Level 2: Some explanation of three or four of the properties, in terms of their structure and bonding, is given. *[3 to 4 marks]*

Level 3: Clear and detailed explanation of all three of the properties, in terms of their structure and bonding, is given. *[5 to 6 marks]*

Here are some points your answer may include:

Diamond

Each carbon atom in diamond forms four covalent bonds in a rigid giant covalent structure/tetrahedral lattice, making it very hard.

Because it is made up of lots of covalent bonds, which take a lot of energy to break, diamond has a very high melting point.

There are no free/delocalised electrons in the structure of diamond, so it can't conduct electricity.

Graphite

Each carbon atom in graphite forms three covalent bonds, creating sheets of carbon atoms that can slide over each other. The carbon layers are only held together weakly, which is what makes graphite soft and slippery.

The covalent bonds between the carbon atoms take a lot of energy to break, giving graphite a very high melting point.

Only three out of each carbon's four outer electrons are used in bonds, so graphite has lots of free/delocalised electrons and can conduct electricity.

192

3.1 Any two from: e.g. have a lid on the beaker / use insulation (e.g. cotton wool) around the beaker / use a polystyrene beaker *[1 mark for each correct answer]*.

3.2 1 °C *[1 mark]*

3.3 37.5 °C *[1 mark]*

3.4 Temperature change = final temperature – initial temperature
= 37.5 – 17 = **20.5 °C**
*[2 marks for correct answer, otherwise 1 mark for writing a correct expression for calculating the temperature change.]*
*If your answer to 4.3 was wrong, you can still have both marks for correctly subtracting 17 from it to find the temperature change.*

3.5 The reaction was exothermic as the temperature of the surroundings increased during the reaction *[1 mark]*.

4.1 Reaction D *[1 mark]*. The most reactive metal will react fastest with the acid *[1 mark]*. In reaction D the largest volume of gas has been collected in the syringe / the most bubbles are being given off *[1 mark]*.

4.2 e.g. zinc *[1 mark]*
*You would get this mark if you named any metal between magnesium and iron in the reactivity series (for example, aluminium would be fine here too).*

4.3

| | Did any reaction occur with: | | |
|---|---|---|---|
| | iron sulfate | magnesium sulfate | copper sulfate |
| **iron** | No | No | Yes |
| **magnesium** | Yes | No | Yes |
| **copper** | No | No | No |

*[1 mark for each correct answer]*

4.4 $Mg_{(s)} + Cu^{2+}_{(aq)} \rightarrow Mg^{2+}_{(aq)} + Cu_{(s)}$
*[1 mark for the correct reactants, 1 mark for the correct products]*

5.1 $ZnCl_2$ *[1 mark]*

5.2 How to grade your answer:
Level 0: There is no relevant information *[No marks]*
Level 1: Statements showing some understanding of the method with some techniques named.
*[1 to 2 marks]*
Level 2: Brief description of the main steps of preparation in order, including filtration, evaporation/ crystallisation and drying.
*[3 to 4 marks]*
Level 3: Detailed description of all correct steps in order.
*[5 to 6 marks]*.
Here are some points your answer may include:
Addition of zinc oxide to hydrochloric acid
Gently warm the dilute hydrochloric acid using a Bunsen burner, then turn off the Bunsen burner.
Add the zinc oxide a bit at a time until no more reacts.
The zinc oxide is now in excess.
Filtration to remove excess zinc oxide
Pour the mixture into a filter funnel lined with filter paper and collect the aqueous solution of zinc chloride.
Crystallisation
Heat the solution using a water bath or an electric heater to evaporate some of the water.
Leave the solution to cool, allowing crystals of zinc chloride to form.
Drying
Filter the zinc chloride crystals out of the remaining solution and leave the crystals to dry.

5.3 sodium chloride *[1 mark]*

5.4 carbon dioxide *[1 mark]*

5.5 E.g. test a sample of the solution using universal indicator paper / test the solution using a pH probe. If the paper turns green / the probe shows a pH of seven, then the solution is neutral. *[1 mark for any sensible method you could use to test the pH of the solution, 1 mark for a correct, matching observation of what that method would show if the solution was neutral.]*

6.1 Oxygen is being removed from the metal oxide / $Fe^{3+}$ ions (iron(III) ions) are gaining electrons *[1 mark]*.

6.2 $M_r$ of $Fe_2O_3 = (2 \times 56) + (3 \times 16) = 160$
Moles of $Fe_2O_3$ = mass ÷ $M_r$ = 40 ÷ 160 = 0.25
From the balanced equation you know that 2 moles of $Fe_2O_3$ produce 4 moles of Fe. So 0.25 moles of $Fe_2O_3$ will produce 0.25 × 2 = 0.50 moles of Fe.
Mass of Fe = moles × $A_r$ = 0.50 × 56 = **28 g**
*[4 marks for correct answer, otherwise 1 mark for $M_r$ of $Fe_2O_3$, 1 mark for number of moles of $Fe_2O_3$, 1 mark for number of moles of Fe.]*

6.3 Aluminium is more reactive than carbon/above carbon in the reactivity series *[1 mark]*. Reduction with carbon can only be used to extract metals that are less reactive than carbon/below carbon in the reactivity series *[1 mark]*.

6.4 In pure iron, the atoms are arranged in layers *[1 mark]*. These layers can slide over each other freely *[1 mark]*. Steel also contains carbon atoms, which are a different size to the iron atoms *[1 mark]*. The carbon atoms distort the layers, so they can't slide over one another so easily *[1 mark]*.

7.1 In a solution of copper sulfate, the ions are free to move and carry an electric current *[1 mark]*. When copper sulfate is solid, the ions are held in fixed positions and can't move *[1 mark]*.

7.2 $Cu^{2+}$, $SO_4^{2-}$, $H^+$, $OH^-$ *[1 mark]*
*The $Cu^{2+}$ and $SO_4^{2-}$ ions come from the ionic compound.*
*The $H^+$ and $OH^-$ ions come from the water.*

7.3 $4OH^- \rightarrow O_2 + 2H_2O + 4e^-$ *[1 mark]*

7.4 Mean change of mass for negative electrode
= (2.36 + 2.71 + 2.55) ÷ 3 = **2.54** *[1 mark]*

7.5 At the negative electrode, copper ions/$Cu^{2+}$ ions are being reduced to copper metal/Cu *[1 mark]*. The half equation for this reaction is: $Cu^{2+} + 2e^- \rightarrow Cu$ *[1 mark]*. So a layer of copper metal forms on the negative electrode during the electrolysis *[1 mark]*.

7.6 The negative electrode would change in mass by twice as much *[1 mark]*.

## Practice Paper 2
### Pages 168-184

1.1

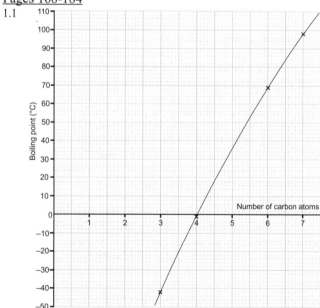

*[1 mark for all four points correctly plotted, 1 mark for a smooth curve that passes through all the points]*

1.2 36 °C *[1 mark for any answer in the range 34-38 °C]*

1.3 $C_nH_{2n+2}$ *[1 mark]*

1.4

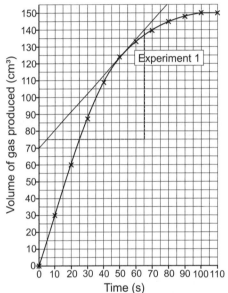

H—C—C—C—H with H H H on top, H H H on bottom *[1 mark]*

1.5 Add a few drops of bromine water to both compounds and shake *[1 mark]*. With propane, nothing will happen *[1 mark]*. Propene will decolourise the bromine water / turn the solution from orange to colourless *[1 mark]*.

1.6 $C_3H_8 + 5O_2 \rightarrow 3CO_2 + \mathbf{4H_2O}$
*[1 mark for correctly giving $H_2O$ as the missing product, 1 mark for correct number of moles of $H_2O$.]*

2.1 As the level of nitrogen dioxide increases, the severity of asthma attacks increases / there is a positive correlation between nitrogen dioxide levels and severity of asthma attacks *[1 mark]*

2.2 The sample of people that the scientists collected data from was too big *[1 mark]*.

2.3 Oxides of nitrogen are formed when nitrogen and oxygen from the air react at high temperatures *[1 mark]*. This happens in car engines (which operate at high enough temperatures for nitrogen oxides to form) *[1 mark]*. In cities, there are lots of cars, so the levels of nitrogen oxides tend to be higher *[1 mark]*.

2.4 e.g. sulfur dioxide *[1 mark]*

3.1 E.g. they don't have enough fresh water / groundwater / surface water to treat and use as drinking water *[1 mark]*.

3.2 Desalination *[1 mark]*

3.3 How to grade your answer:
Level 0: There is no relevant information *[No marks]*
Level 1: There is a brief description of the method to distil seawater, but many details are missing or incorrect. *[1 to 2 marks]*
Level 2: There is some explanation of the method used to distil sea water. Most of the information is correct, but a few small details may be incorrect or missing. *[3 to 4 marks]*
Level 3: There is a clear, detailed and fully correct explanation of the method used to distil sea water in the lab. *[5 to 6 marks]*
Here are some points your answer may include:
Pour the sea water into a (round bottom) flask.
Attach the flask to a condenser and secure both with clamps.
Connect a supply of cold water to the condenser.
Place a beaker under the condenser to collect the fresh water.
Place a Bunsen burner under the round bottom flask and heat the sea water slowly.
The water will boil and form steam.
The steam will condense back to pure liquid water in the condenser and be collected in the beaker as it runs out.
Continue to heat the (round bottom) flask until you have collected a reasonable amount of pure water.

3.4 Large bits of material (such as grit) are removed from the sewage *[1 mark]*.

3.5 The effluent undergoes aerobic biological treatment *[1 mark]*. Air is added to encourage aerobic bacteria to break down any organic matter that is present *[1 mark]*.

4.1 nitrogen *[1 mark]*

4.2 Algae and plants evolved to carry out photosynthesis *[1 mark]*. During photosynthesis carbon dioxide is absorbed, so the amount of carbon dioxide in the atmosphere decreased *[1 mark]*. Photosynthesis also produces oxygen, so the amount of oxygen in the atmosphere increased *[1 mark]*.

4.3 Deforestation — e.g. plants take carbon dioxide out of the atmosphere, so removing trees causes carbon dioxide levels to rise *[1 mark]*.
Increased energy consumption — e.g. burning fossil fuels releases carbon dioxide into the atmosphere *[1 mark]*.
Increasing population — any one from: e.g. more people will be respiring and releasing carbon dioxide / more energy will be used (and carbon dioxide is released when fuels are burnt) / more land will be needed, so trees will have to be cut down, and less carbon dioxide will be removed from the air *[1 mark]*.

4.4 E.g. carbon dioxide is a greenhouse gas *[1 mark]*, so an increase in carbon dioxide in the atmosphere could lead to an increase in global temperatures/global warming *[1 mark]*. As temperatures rise, global food production could decrease due to more extreme weather events / loss of farming land available / water shortages *[1 mark]*.

5.1 Any two from: e.g. volume of acid / size of solid particles / temperature *[1 mark for each correct answer]*

5.2 Draw a tangent to the graph at 50 s, e.g.:

Then find the gradient of your tangent, e.g.:
Gradient of tangent $= \dfrac{\text{change in } y}{\text{change in } x} = \dfrac{(140 - 75)}{(65 - 5)}$
$= 65 \div 60 = 1.08...$
units $= cm^3 \div s = cm^3/s$
rate of reaction at 50 s $= \mathbf{1.1\ cm^3/s}$ (2 s.f.)
*[4 marks in total — 1 mark for a correctly drawn tangent, 1 mark for gradient calculation, 1 mark for correct answer in the range 1 - 1.2, 1 mark for correct units]*

5.3 The gradient of the graph at the start of the reaction is steeper for Experiment 2 *[1 mark]*.

5.4 Increasing the concentration of a reactant increases the number of particles of that substance in the reaction mixture *[1 mark]*. This increases the frequency of collisions between particles of the reactants, increasing the rate of the reaction *[1 mark]*.

5.5 $((0.39 + 0.55 + 0.45) \div 3) = \mathbf{0.46\ g}$ (2 s.f.)
*[2 marks for correct answer, otherwise 1 mark for writing a correct expression that could be used to find the mean.]*

5.6 The gas is carbon dioxide *[1 mark]*. The student should bubble the gas through/shake the gas with an aqueous solution of calcium hydroxide/lime water *[1 mark]*. If carbon dioxide is present the solution will turn cloudy *[1 mark]*.

6.1    How to grade your answer:

Level 0:    No relevant information. *[No marks]*

Level 1:    Response shows a basic understanding that more energy is used in mining and extracting metals from ores compared to recycling metals. An attempt is made to explain why recycling metals is more sustainable. *[1 to 2 marks]*

Level 2:    Response gives a clear understanding that more energy is used in mining and extracting metals from ores compared to recycling metals. Clear reasons are given for why recycling metals is more sustainable. *[3 to 4 marks]*

Level 3:    A clear and detailed response is given which demonstrates a clear understanding that more energy is used in mining and extracting metals from ores compared to recycling metals. The response gives clear and detailed ideas that support why recycling metals is more sustainable. *[5 to 6 marks]*.

Here are some points your answer may include:

Recycling of metals such as aluminium uses only a fraction of the energy required to extract new metals from ores.

Energy used to extract and recycle metals can come from burning fossil fuels which releases gases that contribute to global warming.

As the recycling of metals uses less energy than mining and extracting new metal it can result in less pollution being released into the environment.

Recycling metals conserves the amount of metal ores, which are finite resources, in the earth and this means the use of these metals is more sustainable.

Recycling metals also reduces the amount of waste which goes to landfill.

6.2    Plants are grown in soil that contains copper *[1 mark]*. The plants can't use or get rid of the copper so it accumulates in their leaves *[1 mark]*. The plants can then be dried and burnt, which produces ash containing soluble copper compounds *[1 mark]*. Copper can then be extracted from these compounds by electrolysis / displacement using scrap iron *[1 mark]*.

7.1    The forward and reverse reactions are happening at exactly the same rate *[1 mark]*.

7.2    Le Chatelier's principle states that if you change the conditions of a reversible reaction at equilibrium the system will try to counteract that change *[1 mark]*.

7.3    The yield of sulfur trioxide will increase *[1 mark]*. When pressure is increased the position of equilibrium moves towards the side with fewer gas molecules *[1 mark]*. There are two molecules of gas on the right, compared to three on the left, so the position of equilibrium will move to the right *[1 mark]*.

7.4    catalyst *[1 mark]*

7.5    E.g. 15% of 7500 kg = 7500 × 0.15 = 1125 kg
new mass made in a day = 7500 + 1125 = 8625 kg
new mass made in 5 days = 8625 × 5 = **43 125 kg**
*[3 marks for correct answer, otherwise 1 mark for finding the new mass made in a day and 1 mark for multiplying it by five to find the new mass made in five days.]*

# Index

# Index